Biblioquiz
or, what do you know

?

It is amazing
how little literature there is in the world
SAMUEL JOHNSON

Howard Collins

Biblioquiz
or
what do you know?

Phoenix House
London

an
enter-
tainment

for
book-
lovers

The questions and answers
in this book have appeared in
*The Saturday Review
of Literature*

*Made 1948 in Great Britain. Set, machined and bound by
Purnell and Sons, Ltd., Paulton, Somerset, and London for*

PHOENIX HOUSE LIMITED
38 William IV Street, London, W.C.2.

First published in Great Britain 1948

Contents

1 First Lines of Famous Poems
2 What the Well-dressed Character Wears
3 Famous Words of Famous People
4 Gentlemen of the Cloth
5 Gilbert and Sullivan
6 Favourite Foods of Famous People
7 Twenty Questions
8 Fiction's Famous Servants
9 Card Players in Literature
10 Characters who Wept
11 Three-word Quotations
12 Characters who were Drowned
13 Characters and Hats
14 Dickens Characters
15 Second Lines of Famous Poems
16 As the Curtain Falls
17 Musicians in Literature
18 Lies and Liars
19 Unique Combinations
20 In the Nick of Time
21 Characters who Hid Themselves
22 Sherlock Holmes
23 Actors and Actresses
24 Portable Equipment
25 Unusual First Names of Characters
26 Famous Animals
27 Four-Word Quotations
28 Doctors in Literature
29 Characters Concerned with Bridges
30 Money in Literature

31 Some Interrupted Weddings
32 First Lines of Famous Poems
33 Who is She?
34 Twice-married Men
35 Unusual Hiding Places
36 'The Face is Familiar . . .'
37 Familiar Lines of Famous Poems
38 Transportation in Fiction
39 Alice in Wonderland
40 Songs and their Singers
41 A Patchwork Poem
42 Statues in Literature
43 Elopers in Literature
44 Criminals in Literature
45 Characters who had Unusual Powers
46 Famous Soldiers
47 Numbers in Titles
48 Lines that Precede Famous Lines
49 A Mother Goose Quiz
50 Ten Famous Detectives
51 Place Names in Poetry
52 Shakespeare's Opening Lines
53 Characters who Were Shipwrecked
54 Poets in Literature
55 Famous Ghost Stories
56 Fiction's Famous Funerals
57 Twenty Famous Pen Names
58 Artists in Literature
59 Brothers and Sisters
60 Clocks and Watches
61 It Could Happen to You!
62 Aspects of Nature in Poetry
63 The Sailor's Life
64 Memorable Words of Dickens Characters
65 Chapter Headings

66 Titles Taken from Shakespeare
67 How Well-known Novels End
68 I Felt Such a *Fool!*
69 First Words of Famous Quatrains
70 Characters and Windows
71 Antecedents of ' They '
72 Short-Story Openings
73 Some Famous Sisters
74 Sub-Titles of Well-known Books
75 Characters Concerned with Flowers
76 ' It's the Syme the Whole World Over '
77 Last Lines of Sonnets
78 Twice-married Women
79 Characters who were Disguised
80 In the Middle of the Night
81 Fathers and Sons
82 How to Begin a Novel
83 Requests of Poets
84 Gifts in Literature
85 Characters who were very Sick
86 Repeated Words and Phrases
87 Who is ' He '?
88 Scrambled Names of Dickens Characters

Answers
will be found at the back
of the book

Questions

1 · First Lines of Famous Poems. *Here are the first lines of twenty well-known poems. Can you identify each poem and name the poet who wrote it?*

1 A garden is a lovesome thing, God wot!
2 A thing of beauty is a joy for ever.
3 Comrades, leave me here a while, while as yet 'tis early morn.
4 Drink to me only with thine eyes.
5 Gather ye rosebuds while ye may.
6 Go and catch a falling star.
7 Grow old along with me!
8 Hail to thee, blithe spirit!
9 Hence, loathèd Melancholy!
10 It is a beauteous evening, calm and free.
11 Let us go hence, my songs; she will not hear.
12 My hair is grey, but not with years.
13 The blessed damozel leaned out.
14 The curfew tolls the knell of parting day.
15 The sea is calm tonight.
16 The skies they were ashen and sober.
17 The stag at eve had drunk his fill.
18 'Tis the middle of night by the castle clock.
19 We caught the tread of dancing feet.
20 With rue my heart is laden.

2 · What the Well-dressed Character Wears. *Clothes may not make the man but often they do make literary characters linger in our memories. From these descriptions of their distinctive wearing apparel can you identify the characters and name the stories in which they appear?*

1 After being jilted on her wedding night, she continued thereafter to wear her wedding dress, lace veil, satin shoes, and bridal flowers.

2 Needing a new dress for a business trip, she made one out of some green velvet curtains.

3 He'd a French cocked hat on his forehead, a bunch of lace at his chin, a coat of the claret velvet, and breeches of brown doe-skin.

4 In a mistaken attempt to win his lady love, he wore yellow stockings and crossed garters, a garb which she loathed.

5 At a fancy-dress ball she wore a single rose twined in her hair, a dress contrived out of a few old newspapers and the inside of an umbrella, a bag string around her waist, and a piece of old lace suspended from her hair.

6 The uniform 'e wore was nothin' much before an' rather less than 'arf o' that be'ind.

7 Condemned for life to wear a scarlet 'A' upon her breast, this seamstress did a fancy job, making the letter of scarlet cloth embroidered in gold thread.

8 He wore a red coat, blue trousers, and purple shoes with crimson soles and crimson linings.

9 His queer long coat from heel to head was half of yellow and half of red.

10 He wore a beautiful cravat (or was it a belt?) that had been given to him by the king as an un-birthday present.

3 · Famous Words of Famous People. *Of course you remember the famous speeches from the pages of literature quoted below. But can you also remember who spoke them?*

1 'To thine own self be true, and it shall follow, as the night the day, thou canst not then be false to any man.'

2 'It is a far, far better thing that I do than I have ever done; it is a far, far better rest that I go to than I have ever known.'

3 'One, if by land, and two, if by sea, and I on the opposite shore will be, ready to ride and spread the alarm.'

4 'And how can man die better than facing fearful odds for the ashes of his fathers and the temples of his Gods?'

5 'Parting is such sweet sorrow that I shall say goodnight till it be morrow.'

6 'You mentioned your name as if I should recognize it, but beyond the obvious facts that you are a bachelor, a solicitor, a Freemason, and an asthmatic, I know nothing whatever about you.'

7 'When *I* use a word, it means just what I choose it to mean—neither more nor less.'

8 'I shouldn't be sufficiently degraded in my own estimation unless I was insulted by a very considerable bribe.'

9 'All the world's a stage, and all the men and women merely players.'

10 'Annual income twenty pounds, annual expenditure nineteen nineteen six, result happiness; annual income twenty pounds, annual expenditure twenty pounds ought and six, result misery.'

11 'Here's your good health, and your family's, and may they live long and prosper!'

12 'This rock shall fly from its firm base as soon as I!'

13 'My soul ain't yours! It's been bought and paid for by One that is able to keep it. Ye may kill my body but ye can't harm my soul.'

14 'I'll come to thee by moonlight, though hell should bar the way!'

15 'I pray thee, then, write me as one who loves his fellow men.'

16 'God's in his heaven; all's right with the world.'

17 'I chose my wife, as she did her wedding gown, not for a fine glossy surface, but such qualities as would wear well.'

18 'Be careful to be guided by this golden rule: Stick close to your desks and never go to sea and you all may be rulers of the Queen's Navee.'

3

4 · Gentlemen of the Cloth. *From the earliest times to the present the clergy have been prominent in the world's literature. Can you identify the ten members described below and name the stories in which they appeared?*

1 He bore the loss of his fortune, the seduction of his daughter, the burning of his home, and imprisonment for debt with unruffled cheerfulness.

2 After seven years of worrying about it, this minister publicly confessed his adultery.

3 He united in marriage the children of two hostile Italian families.

4 With the help of a simple-minded but fervent disciple, this young hermit put the devil in hell.

5 A gluttonous hypocrite, he persuaded a simple-minded husband to give him his fortune and his daughter and then tried to seduce his wife.

6 After proposing three times to Elizabeth Bennet, this humourless and formal-mannered rector married her dearest friend.

7 This zealous but nearly blind missionary mistook an island of penguins for humans and baptized them.

8 During a famine this bishop assembled the poor people in a barn and burned them to death in order to have more food for the rich, and was presently punished when an army of rats swarmed into his tower and devoured him.

9 This village priest allowed such crimes as murder, burglary, forgery, and kidnapping to be expiated at half-a-crown apiece, but he frowned on flirtations.

10 This zealous and narrow-minded missionary, unavoidably detained on a South Sea island in the company of a prostitute, reformed her—and then wished he hadn't.

5 · Gilbert and Sullivan. *Gilbert and Sullivan fans should have little trouble in identifying the sixteen characters in this quiz from these brief self-descriptions.*

1 'I am never known to quail at the fury of a gale, and I'm never never sick at sea.'

2 'I'm very good at integral and differential calculus; I know the scientific names of beings animalculous.'

3 'I have a left shoulder-blade that is a miracle of loveliness. People come miles to see it. My right elbow has a fascination few can resist.'

4 'I'm not so old, and not so plain, and I'm quite prepared to marry again.'

5 'When I was a lad I served a term as office boy to an attorney's firm.'

6 'Though counting in the usual way, years twenty-one I've been alive, yet, reckoning by my natal day, I am a little boy of five!'

7 'A wandering minstrel I—a thing of shreds and patches.'

8 'On Tuesday I made a false income-tax return. On Wednesday I forged a will. On Thursday I shot a fox. On Friday I forged a cheque.'

9 'All thieves who could my fees afford relied on my orations, and many a burglar I've restored to his friends and his relations.'

10 'A many years ago, when I was young and charming, as some of you may know, I practised baby-farming.'

11 'A nurserymaid is not afraid of what you people *call* work, so I made up my mind to go as a kind of piratical maid-of-all-work.'

12 'I can trace my ancestry back to a protoplasmal primordial atomic globule. Consequently, my family pride is something inconceivable. I can't help it. I was born sneering.'

13 'In an enterprise of martial kind, when there was any fighting, he led his regiment from behind—he found it less exciting.'

14 'Am I alone and unobserved? I am! Then let me own I'm an aesthetic sham! This air severe is but a mere veneer!'

15 'I've an irritating chuckle, I've a celebrated sneer, I've an entertaining snigger, I've a fascinating leer.'

16 'Sometimes I sit and wonder, in my artless Japanese way, why it is that I am so much more attractive than anybody else in the whole world.'

6 · Favourite Foods of Famous People. *Do you recall the dietetic peculiarities of the well-known literary characters that are mentioned below?*

1 When Cock Robin proposed to Jenny Wren, he promised that she should dine on (*a*) candied sunflower seeds (*b*) curds and whey (*c*) plum cake and sugar candy (*d*) cherry pie and currant wine (*e*) hot cross buns.

2 The feast that Barmecide served to a starving beggar was (*a*) meatless (*b*) uncooked (*c*) rich and rare (*d*) poisoned (*e*) imaginary.

3 During office hours, Nero Wolfe, the huge detective, sits at his desk and drinks vast quantities of (*a*) beer (*b*) black coffee (*c*) water (*d*) milk (*e*) bromo seltzer.

4 Prince Florizel of Bohemia was intrigued into joining the Suicide Club by a young man who had just spent the last of his fortune on (*a*) a round of champagne for the house (*b*) several dozen cream tarts (*c*) a sack of salted peanuts (*d*) a dish of pickled onions (*e*) a glass of tomato juice and a couple of aspirin tablets.

5 The wife of the Vicar of Wakefield was widely known for the excellence of her (*a*) pork pies (*b*) stuffed sausage (*c*) gooseberry wine (*d*) chocolate layer cake (*e*) apple dumplings.

6 During the three years that Ben Gunn was marooned on Treasure Island he dreamed of eating (*a*) toasted cheese (*b*) roast goose (*c*) fish and chips (*d*) stuffed celery (*e*) plum pudding.

7 After his encounter with the tigers, Little Black Sambo was so hungry that he ate (*a*) 11 tiger steaks (*b*) 24 barbecued pork chops (*c*) 17 coconut pies (*d*) 87 water melons (*e*) 169 pancakes.

8 After devouring a cake on which the words EAT ME were beautifully marked in currants, Alice (*a*) became so small that she had to swim in the tears she had shed not long before (*b*) expanded like a telescope until she was nine feet tall (*c*) couldn't remember her name (*d*) was able to go through the looking glass (*e*) became a queen.

9 Algernon Moncrieff invited his aunt to tea, but before she arrived he had eaten all of the (*a*) caviare (*b*) macaroons (*c*) crumpets (*d*) scones (*e*) cucumber sandwiches.

10 After Timon of Athens had squandered his fortune on fair weather friends, he invited them to a banquet and served nothing but (*a*) bean soup (*b*) burnt bread (*c*) mashed potatoes (*d*) meat bones (*e*) luke-warm water.

7 · Twenty Questions. *Here's a new variety of a popular parlour game. Listed below are twenty questions that have been asked by twenty famous poets. You don't have to give the answers; just name the poets.*

1 What is so rare as a day in June?
2 O Wind, if Winter comes, can Spring be far behind?
3 Who loosened and let down this brutal jaw?
4 How do you like to go up in a swing, up in the air so blue?
5 Shall I compare thee to a summer's day?
6 What immortal hand or eye dare frame thy fearful symmetry?
7 O cuckoo! shall I call thee bird, or but a wandering voice?
8 How doth the little busy bee improve each shining hour?
9 Why so pale and wan, fond lover?
10 Was it a vision, or a waking dream?
11 Have you heard of the wonderful one-hoss shay that was built in such a logical way it ran a hundred years to a day?
12 Can storied urn or animated bust back to its mansion call the fleeting breath?
13 The night is chill, the forest bare; is it the wind that moaneth bleak?
14 Cats may have had their goose cooked by tobacco-juice, still, why deny its use, thoughtfully taken?
15 Doth God exact day labour, light denied?
16 Where are the snows of yesteryear?
17 How does the water come down at Lodore?
18 Rose kissed me today. Will she kiss me tomorrow?
19 What passion cannot Music raise and quell?
20 What is this life if, full of care, we have no time to stand and stare?

8 · Fiction's Famous Servants. *Here are ten literary figures whose careers as servants have made them immortal. Can you identify them and name the authors who created them?*

1 A water carrier in the service of Her Majesty's army in India, he was killed in action.

2 The perfect butler, he exercised an iron hand on the raiment and love life of Bertie Wooster, his employer.

3 Inspired by a couple of crooked lawyers, this landlady brought suit for breach of promise against her gentleman lodger.

4 When a gang of thieves plotted to surprise and kill her master by hiding in a bunch of jars, this servant saved his life by pouring boiling oil on them.

5 He was the butler in the service of Lady Verinder, and *Robinson Crusoe* served as his Bible.

6 When this romantic novel-reading servant girl married the hired man, he undertook to cure her of her fantastic notions by honeymooning in an insane asylum.

7 This butler was once in the employ of an English nobleman, who lost him, in a poker game, to a Western American millionaire.

8 Because she was slightly deaf, this nurserymaid mistakenly apprenticed the boy in her charge to a pirate instead of a pilot.

9 She kept house for a consulting detective and a retired army doctor.

10 Though the villain pursued her and pursued her, her virtue was rewarded when he married her in the end.

9 · Card Players in Literature. *This quiz concerns ten assorted characters to whom card playing was of more-than-ordinary importance. Can you identify them and name the authors who created them?*

1 This impoverished law clerk beguiled his evenings by playing cribbage with himself for fifty thousand pounds a game until he caught the servant girl watching him through a keyhole and taught her to play.

2 Although this London clubman travelled round the world, he did little sight-seeing for he was more interested in playing whist.

3 While this charming young lady was concentrating on a three-handed game of ombre, an admirer snipped off a lock of her hair.

4 Although he maintained that he did not understand how to play euchre, this wily oriental, whose sleeves were stuffed with extra cards, trimmed a couple of card sharpers.

5 Playing whist was her life business; her duty; the thing she came into the world to do, and she did it; she unbent her mind afterwards over a book.

6 As he was playing solo whist in a Malamute saloon, this gambler was shot by a piano-playing prospector.

7 Three times the cards went round the table, and on the fourth round there fell to this Bohemian prince the ace of spades—which meant that he was to be murdered that night.

8 Among his many fields of learning this dilettante detective included an unerring knowledge of poker, which he used to trap a murderer.

9 Faro was not a game with him—it was at once his profession, his science, his drug, his drink, his mistress; and in one year of playing it in Chicago he lost his wife's ten thousand dollar inheritance.

10 During a winning streak this poker player would often go a week without sleep, but after a stretch of bad luck he wrote his epitaph on the deuce of clubs and shot himself.

10 · **Characters who Wept.** *The following literary figures were noted for shedding tears. Can you identify them and name the author who created each?*

1 This yellow-haired maiden yearning for her lover from the rampart of Heaven lays her head between her hands and weeps because she must wait for him.

2 This young orphan girl riding on the chaise to Durham weeps inconsolably for her ragged cloak which has become entangled in the wheel.

3 After her brothers kill and bury this woman's lover she disinters his body, cuts off the head, and places it in a garden-pot which she waters with her tears.

4 This character sheds copious tears because of the fate which his appetite has ordained for a number of unsuspecting bivalves.

5 This boy, the youngest of a large patriarchal family, can cry at will to further his own designing purposes; he simply closes his eyes tight and murmurs the magic formula: 'Oh, how terrible! How terrible!'

6 After she is deserted by her husband, this broken-hearted nymph tearfully calls upon 'mother Ida' to hear her tale of woe before she dies.

7 This character, seeing the grief of his master who discovers that he has fought and killed in combat his own son, in mute woe sheds big warm tears from dark compassionate eyes.

8 This woman, sick for home, stood in tears amid the alien corn.

9 This sweet, brown-haired girl wept with delight when her schoolmate gave her a smile.

10 After losing her dowry with her brother at sea, this noble lady of 'the moated grange' was cast off by her fiancé, who, washed with her tears, remained as marble to them.

11 · Three-word Quotations. *Printed below are twenty three-word phrases which have been lifted out of as many well-known poems. Can you match up each phrase (after making the mental jump to identify the poem from which it was taken) with the poet who wrote it?*

1 *All smiles stopped*   (   ) Matthew Arnold
2 *Distinctly I remember*   (   ) Rupert Brooke
3 *Drink to me*   (   ) Robert Browning
4 *Go, lovely rose*   (   ) Samuel T. Coleridge
5 *Goodbye, proud world*   (   ) Ralph Waldo Emerson
6 *He prayeth best*   (   ) Oliver Goldsmith
7 *I never writ*   (   ) Thomas Gray
8 *Ignorant armies clash*   (   ) Ben Jonson
9 *Know then thyself*   (   ) John Keats
10 *Learn to labour*   (   ) Henry W. Longfellow
11 *Melancholy marked him*   (   ) John McCrae
12 *No birds sing*   (   ) John Milton
13 *Nothing beside remains*   (   ) George Pope Morris
14 *Rivers are damp*   (   ) Dorothy Parker
15 *Rural virtues leave*   (   ) Edgar Allan Poe
16 *Spare that tree*   (   ) Alexander Pope
17 *The poppies blow*   (   ) William Shakespeare
18 *They also serve*   (   ) Percy Bysshe Shelley
19 *Think only this*   (   ) Edmund Waller
20 *We are seven*   (   ) William Wordsworth

12 · Characters Who Were Drowned. *All of the characters in this quiz met death by drowning. Can you identify each as well as the story in which he appeared?*

1 During a fog and flood on the Mississippi, when his showboat had struck a snag, this captain fell off the bridge and drowned.

2 This fisherman was drowned while attempting to rescue from a stricken ship the man who had betrayed his fiancée.

3 Although he kept an artificial respirator on hand for emergencies, this brain surgeon drowned because at the moment he needed it the respirator was being used on a wealthy playboy.

4 So modest was this maiden that, rather than remove her clothes so a sailor could swim to shore with her from a wrecked ship, she stayed on board and went down.

5 'O no! Then list with fearful eye, whilst I his fate do tell: his soul did from this cold world fly by falling down a well. They got him out and emptied him; alas it was too late; his spirit was gone for to sport aloft in the realms of the good and great.'

6 Lost in a snow storm, this little girl walked off a bridge and into a watery grave.

7 Unhinged by her father's sudden death at the hands of her fiancé who was apparently going batty, she fell into a brook and didn't know enough to come out.

8 Stubbing her toe upon a sliver, this prospector's daughter fell in the river and drowned.

9 During a raging flood she set out in a rowing boat to rescue her estranged brother and drowned in his arms when the boat was sunk.

10 After harpooning a whale, this captain was caught in the harpoon's line and dragged out of the boat to drown.

13 · Characters and Hats. *Here are ten literary characters who are associated with hats of various kinds. Can you identify each character and name the author who created him?*

1 Because he resented the visiting rector's calling him a 'little gentleman', this boy filled his bowler hat with fresh tar.

2 To induce a green-eyed war-widow to abandon her unbecoming mourning, this smuggler gave her a Paris bonnet made of dark green taffeta and trimmed with green ribbons and a green ostrich plume.

3 After a quarrel with his lady-love this gentleman rushed out of her residence but had to return to get his hat.

4 The first time and the last time the story-teller saw this unhappy heroine she was wearing a green felt sports hat.

5 From a close inspection of a seedy-looking derby, this detective deduced that its owner was highly intellectual, was well-to-do until recently, had taken to drink, led a sedentary life, was middle-aged, used lime-cream on his hair which he had had cut within three days, lived in a house not supplied with gas, and that his wife had ceased to love him.

6 This criminological clergyman always wears a broad slouch hat and carries an umbrella.

7 On his first day in Osage, Oklahoma, he had his large white sombrero shot off his head by some citizens who didn't like its colour.

8 This tyrant had his cap placed on a pole in front of the new prison and decreed that all passers-by salute it.

9 When a frustrated income tax collector, distracted by some pet snakes, left behind a panama sized seven and an eighth, this elderly gentleman decided to keep it.

10 This quarrelsome person wore a top hat on which was a sign reading: 'In this style 10/6'.

14 · Dickens Characters. *In this Dickens quiz, score yourself* 1 *point for each A item correctly answered,* 2 *points for the B items,* 3 *points for C items, and* 4 *for D items. Anyone should be able to get a score of* 10; *you know some Dickens if you can reach* 30; *you're quite an expert if your score is* 50; *and you're out of this world—and in the world of Dickens—if you can get over* 70.

1 What Dickens hero worked for (*a*) an undertaker, (*b*) a theatrical troupe, (*c*) a proctor, (*d*) a retired dustman?

2 What Dickens character ran a school in (*a*) Yorkshire, (*b*) Canterbury, (*c*) Brighton, (*d*) Cloisterham?

3 What Dickens character earned a living by (*a*) exhibiting waxworks, (*b*) being a locksmith, (*c*) running a horse-riding circus, (*d*) conducting a dressmaking establishment?

4 What Dickens character played (*a*) the flute, (*b*) the organ, (*c*) the clarionet, (*d*) the kit?

5 What Dickens character was forced to use (*a*) a crutch, (*b*) a claw for a hand, (*c*) one wooden leg, (*d*) two wooden legs?

6 What Dickens character died of (*a*) decapitation, (*b*) spontaneous combustion, (*c*) a fall into an abandoned pit, (*d*) chronic alcoholism?

7 What Dickens character was murdered by (*a*) a brutal burglar, (*b*) a French maid, (*c*) his partner in a fraudulent insurance company, (*d*) his steward?

8 What Dickens character married (*a*) a pretended sportsman, (*b*) a young doctor, (*c*) a writer of novels, (*d*) a barrister without clients?

9 What Dickens character, who is referred to in the title of the novel in which he plays a part, was born in (*a*) a workhouse, (*b*) a prison, (*c*) a fashionable London mansion, (*d*) a caul?

10 What Dickens character lived (*a*) in a beached boat, (*b*) at Chesney Wold, (*c*) at the *Maypole*, (*d*) at the *George and Vulture*?

15 · Second Lines of Famous Poems. *Listed below are the second lines of twenty famous poems by as many well-known poets. Can you identify each poem and its author?*

1 And all I ask is a tall ship and a star to steer her by.
2 And he stoppeth one of three.
3 And his cohorts were gleaming with purple and gold.
4 Bird thou never wert.
5 By the Nine Gods he swore.
6 Dig the grave and let me lie.
7 I gallop'd, Dirck gallop'd, we gallop'd all three.
8 I summon up remembrance of things past.
9 On thy cold grey stones, O sea
10 Old Kaspar's work was done.
11 Old Time is still a-flying.
12 One end is moo, the other milk.
13 Prithee, why so pale?
14 Tell her that wastes her time and me.
15 The kid that handles the music box was hitting a jag-time tune.
16 The leaves they were crispèd and sere.
17 The lowing herd winds slowly o'er the lea.
18 The moon was a ghostly galleon tossed upon cloudy seas.
19 The owl, for all his feathers, was a-cold.
20 The ship has weathered every rack, the prize we sought is won.

16 · As the Curtain Falls. *The stage directions given below are taken from the very end of ten well-known plays, after the last speech has been given and before the curtain falls. Can you identify the plays and name their authors?*

1 (*A death march. Exeunt, bearing off the dead bodies after which a peal of ordnance is shot off.*)

2 (*The sound of a door shutting is heard from below.*)

3 (*A sound is heard that seems to come from the sky, like a breaking harp-string, dying away mournfully. All is still again, and there is heard nothing but the strokes of the axe far away in the orchard.*)

4 (*When she has gone the possible meaning of her question startles him. The curtain hides him from us, but we may be sure that he will soon be bland again. We have a comfortable feeling, you and I, that there is nothing of* HARRY SIMS *in us.*)

5 (*She faints upon the ottoman. He pauses for a moment irresolutely —then he goes to the door, opens it, and stands looking out.*)

6 (*The whine of a shell rises to a shriek and bursts on the dug-out roof. The shock stabs out the candle-flame; the timber props of the door cave slowly in, sand bags fall and block the passage to the open air. There is darkness in the dug-out. Here and there the red dawn glows through the jagged holes of the open doorway. Very faintly there comes the dull rattle of machine-guns; and the fevered spatter of rifle fire.*)

7 (*All movement ceases. Seconds of sombre silence pass. A rotten shingle falls from the sagging porch, and the curtain falls slowly.*)

8 (*The lights slowly come up and the whole stage is composed of massive tiers, upon which stand the entire Company. The Union Jack flies over their heads as they sing God Save the King.*)

9 (*He slams his hat on angrily and stalks out.* VINNIE *gives a triumphant nod, and follows him. The curtain starts down, and as it falls,* CLARENCE *again kneels at* MARY'S *feet.*)

10 (WITHERSPOON *bows to the ladies and lifts the glass to his lips, but the curtain falls before he does.*)

17 · Musicians in Literature. *Literary characters often have occasion to demonstrate their musical talents. Do you remember what instrument was played by those mentioned below?*

1 In Keats' *The Eve of St Agnes*, the instrument that Porphyro played to the sleeping Madeline was the

cithara French horn lute saxophone ukelele

2 Supiyawlat, the Burma girl in Kipling's *The Road to Mandalay*, played the

bagpipe banjo flute mouth organ tambourine

3 Sherlock Holmes, as we learn from Dr Watson, was a capable performer on the

clarinet concertina jew's-harp piano violin

4 The Owl who eloped with the Pussy Cat, in the poem by Edward Lear, played a

guitar kettle drum trombone tuba xylophone

5 Because of a morbid acuteness of the senses, the only music that Roderick Usher could bear to hear was that of the

guitar hurdygurdy oboe virginal zither

6 In Molnar's *The Guardsman*, whenever the actress felt the need of a change of lovers she would play the

cello harp ocarina phonograph piano

7 In Browning's *Abt Vogler*, the court chaplain is extemporizing on the

clavichord glockenspiel harp organ piano

8 When Nanki-Poo, son of the Mikado, was disguised as a wandering minstrel, he carried a

Chinese fiddle guitar mandolin musical saw samisen

9 Wild animals, and even rocks and trees, came to listen when Orpheus played his

flageolet harp lute lyre pan pipes

10 The musical obbligato for the Ancient Mariner's tale was furnished by a

bassoon cornet double bass pianoforte sistrum

18 · Lies and Liars. *Here are some of the memorable lies and liars from the pages of literature. How many of them do you recall? Name the character and the story.*

1 To save his girl friend from being whipped for tearing a page in their teacher's medical book, this boy took the blame.

2 He excused his embroidery of a lie by saying that it was 'merely corroborative detail, intended to give artistic verisimilitude to an otherwise bald and unconvincing narrative.'

3 Although her husband had forbidden her to eat macaroons, she ate them anyway, and told him she hadn't.

4 Out of ammunition, this noted tale-spinner shot a stag with some cherry stones, hit him in the head, and found him two years later with a ten-foot cherry tree sprouting between his antlers.

5 Upon discovering that her sister's fiancé was unexpectedly prosperous, she told him that the sister was about to marry another man and then married the gullible victim herself.

6 After dropping her wedding ring down a well, she told her husband, for some obscure reason, that she had lost it at the sea shore.

7 During the siege of Paris in 1870, this elderly invalid, an ex-soldier, was led by his granddaughter and his physician to believe that Berlin, not Paris, was under siege.

8 Stimulated by a whisky-and-soda contributed by a fellow member of the Billiards Club, this gentleman could remember some most amazing adventures.

9 Using the fact that the French windows happened to be wide open, this romantic young lady convinced a caller that her aunt was insane and that her other relatives were dead and haunting the house.

10 This notorious liar was struck dead for lying about the price he received for a piece of land he had sold in order to give the proceeds to the church.

19 · Unique Combinations. *This quiz consists of twenty unique combinations of adjective and noun. Can you match up each combination with the name of the poet who used it?*

1	Beaded bubbles	( ) Matthew Arnold
2	Blithe spirit	( ) George Gordon Byron
3	Brave vibration	( ) Lewis Carroll
4	Committed linnets.	( ) Samuel T. Coleridge
5	Complaining flute	( ) John Dryden.
6	Counterfeited glee	( ) Oliver Goldsmith
7	Demon lover	( ) Thomas Gray
8	Fairest wights	( ) Robert Herrick
9	Fantastic arabesques	( ) Thomas Hood
10	Hot haste	( ) Leigh Hunt
11	Ignorant armies	( ) John Keats
12	Inward eye	( ) Richard Lovelace
13	Livelier iris	( ) John Milton
14	Simple annals	( ) Edgar Allan Poe
15	Starving chemist	( ) Alexander Pope
16	Sweet accord	( ) William Shakespeare
17	Uncertain rustling	( ) Percy Bysshe Shelley
18	Uncessant care	( ) Alfred Tennyson
19	Unwomanly rags	( ) Oscar Wilde
20	Vorpal sword	( ) William Wordsworth

20 · In the Nick of Time. *Here are some characters who were rescued from dire fate in the nick of time. Do you remember the stories and their authors?*

1 Just as this wealthy landowner was about to marry the plain girl he employed as governess, a stranger popped up and stopped the wedding ceremony.

2 The last surviving leader of an Indian tribe sacrifices his life in an unsuccessful attempt to rescue the daughter of an American army officer.

3 A noted sleuth breaks open a coffin in time to rescue one of the occupants, a lady whom the villain had chloroformed.

4 Despite innumerable obstacles, this French military man made his way to England and back in time to deliver the jewels which the Queen was scheduled to wear at a ball.

5 As the heroine approached the gallows on which she was to be hanged for killing her child, her betrayer galloped up waving a reprieve.

6 As a common sailor is about to be thrown into a dungeon it is disclosed that, due to a mix-up on a baby farm, he is actually the captain of the ship.

7 Although impeded by endless police red-tape and stupidity, the heroine finally gets through to the authorities with her vital evidence just in time to stop the hanging of an innocent man for murder.

8 With a king dead drunk on the morning of his coronation, his cousin is persuaded to impersonate him because they look so much alike.

9 Out on a limb and pursued by an angry bear, a traveller is saved at the last moment when his companion fires three accurate arrows from a cross-bow.

10 A Spanish conquistador and his friends, about to be tortured by the Aztecs, are rescued by an Indian once befriended by the hero.

21 · Characters Who Hid Themselves. *For one reason or another, each of the characters in this quiz hid himself. From the circumstances briefly outlined below, can you identify them and name the stories in which they appear?*

1 Aided by a little girl, this lad eluded a band of outlaws by submerging himself in an icy stream.

2 In another man's rooms, and about to be discovered by her husband, she hid behind a curtain and allowed another woman to claim responsibility for her fan, left in plain sight.

3 With the connivance of an agèd serving woman, he hid in the closet adjoining his beloved's bed chamber.

4 On her wedding night this playful young bride hid in a large oak chest, which snapped shut with a spring-lock and stayed that way for fifty years.

5 Abhorred by everyone he met, this man-made monster hid for more than a year in a hovel adjoining a country cottage.

6 Surprised by a suspicious husband, this portly wooer hid in a basket of villainously smelling laundry and was carried out and thrown into the river.

7 With two companions, this boy hid in the unused gallery of a church and listened to the funeral sermon being preached in the belief that they had drowned.

8 While an elderly irate husband searched under the bed, behind the curtains, in the closets, and up the chimney, this youthful lover lay hidden under the covers of his mistress's bed.

9 Hidden at the bottom of an apple barrel, this boy overheard the plans of some mutineers.

10 Fleeing from pursuers after his escape from prison, he hid inside a shallow chest in his fiancée's bedroom while she pretended to be sleeping on top of it, and almost smothered to death.

22 · Sherlock Holmes. *Few characters in fiction are so well known as Sherlock Holmes, whose private life and public career have been the subject of many scholarly treatises. Even if you're not a Baker Street Irregular, you should know most of the answers to the twenty questions below.*

1 What was the title of the first Sherlock Holmes story?

2 At what address did Sherlock Holmes reside during the greater part of his professional career?

3 Who shared the three-room suite with him?

4 What was the name of his landlady?

5 Where did he keep his pipe tobacco?

6 How did he keep from losing his unanswered correspondence?

7 What was his favourite drink?

8 What drug did he take during the early part of his career?

9 What musical instrument did he play?

10 On what period of music was he an authority?

11 What outdoor pastime did he pursue indoors?

12 To what club did he belong?

13 What was the name of his brother?

14 Whom did he consider 'the Napoleon of crime'?

15 What was his first case?

16 Name one of the Scotland Yard detectives with whom he was associated.

17 How many forms of tobacco ash could he distinguish?

18 In the opinion of Sherlock Holmes, what woman eclipsed and predominated over the whole of her sex?

19 In what part of England did Sherlock live after his retirement?

20 What occupation did he take up at that time?

23 · **Actors and Actresses.** *Briefly described below are ten actors and actresses who have appeared in well-known books and plays. Can you recall their names and the stories in which they starred?*

1 One of a group of Athenian business men who were going to present a play about Pyramus and Thisbe, he was cast in the role of the lion.

2 To avoid the embarrassment of appearing in home-made tights at the performance of *The Children's Pageant of the Table Round* this eleven-year-old, just before going on stage, donned the janitor's overalls.

3 This ignorant but entrancing actress captivated the affections of a boy ten years younger than herself.

4 In the role of a Russian guardsman this actor successfully made love to his own wife, but he could never be sure whether she had really penetrated his disguise, as she later claimed.

5 Her actor-parents extolled her phenomenal talents as this very young ballerina rehearsed *The Savage and the Maiden*.

6 Hoping to become another Harold Parmelee, idol of the silver screen, this Simsbury, Illinois, movie aspirant had learned to imitate every one of his hero's typical gestures, but the result was burlesque.

7 When deafness ended the stage career of this celebrated Shakespearian actor, he devoted his talents to amateur crime detection.

8 Only twelve people in a Mississippi river town turned out to see 'David Garrick' and his partner in their Shakespearian repertoire, so he turned to low comedy instead.

9 Infatuated by this beautiful actress, all the undergraduates at Oxford University committed suicide.

10 Between the time she played Nora in a college production of *A Doll's House* and the day her road company closed *Romeo and Juliet* in Pike City, Kansas, this aspiring actress became a real trouper.

24 · Portable Equipment. *Many characters in fiction are closely associated with out-of-the-ordinary objects which they carried about at all times. From these brief descriptions of such objects, can you recognize the characters and name the story in which they appeared?*

1 Not over-bright, this tramp labourer was fond of carrying dead mice in his pocket.

2 Having convinced his subjects that he could be killed only by a silver bullet, this Negro emperor had one cast and carried it in his pocket.

3 This night school student always elaborately printed his name with red, blue, and green crayons.

4 Throughout a long and varied lifetime, the one object with him to the end was a jewelled statue of the Madonna, slightly cracked.

5 In melancholy moods he would get out an X-ray of his girl friend's thorax and look at it.

6 Believe it or not, this Chinese card sharper carried twenty-four packs of playing cards up his sleeves!

7 After an expedition into Kafiristan, he returned to civilization carrying the mummified head of his red-haired companion.

8 Though strictly teetotal, this member of a trio of elderly spinsters was always equipped with a bottle of blackberry cordial for use in emergencies.

9 This elderly sleuth was always fumbling with a piece of knotted string.

10 So fond of tobacco was this pirate captain that he carried a double-jointed cigar holder which enabled him to smoke two cigars at the same time.

25 · Unusual First Names of Characters. *Charles Dickens was not the only author to capitalize upon the fact that giving a character an unusual name has some extra recognition value. Of the fifty-one well-known characters whose first names are listed below, how many can you surname?*

1 Algernon	18 Hercule	35 Rawdon
2 Bathsheba	19 Ichabod	36 Reginald
3 Bigger	20 Jeeter	37 Rhett
4 Bingo	21 Kimball	38 Robinson
5 Clovis	22 Lorna	39 Sancho
6 Colin	23 Manon	40 Scattergood
7 Cosmo	24 Mateo	41 Sheridan
8 Dink	25 Miniver	42 Soames
9 Disko	26 Moll	43 Tanis
10 Doremus	27 Mycroft	44 Tish
11 Edmund	28 Nero	45 Trilby
12 Emmeline	29 Peachey	46 Tristram
13 Enoch	30 Penelope	47 Uriah
14 Fancourt	31 Penrod	48 Wackford
15 Florian	32 Peregrine	49 Wilkins
16 Gavin	33 Pollyanna	50 Yancey
17 Hedda	34 Phileas	51 Zuleika

26 · Famous Animals. *Here are ten well-known animals from the pages of literature. Can you name each one and the story in which he appears?*

1 Disobeying his mother's commands, this little rabbit went into Mr McGregor's garden and lost his shoes and his little blue jacket with the brass buttons.

2 As this little forest deer grew older he discovered that life can be dangerous as well as beautiful.

3 A gypsy girl had trained this pretty white goat with gilt horns and hoofs to count, to give imitations of public personages, and to spell out with wooden blocks the name of the man she loved.

4 Escaping from some Arabs who had taken him prisoner, a French soldier took refuge in a small desert oasis where this female panther fell in love with him.

5 After this old circus lion died of constipation, people paid an extra dime to go inside the cage with him.

6 This gigantic blue ox measured forty-two axe handles and a plug of chewing tobacco between the horns.

7 This little bull went on a sit-down strike.

8 The pride and joy of Lord Emsworth, she won the silver medal in the Fat Pigs class for two years straight.

9 The adventures of this unladylike cat were recorded every night in *vers libre* by a literary cockroach.

10 This giant ferret, responding to the prayers of an imaginative little boy, killed the child's guardian.

27 · Four-word Quotations. *Printed below are twenty four-word sentences which have been lifted out of as many well-known poems. Can you match up each sentence (after making a mental jump to identify the poem from which it was taken) with the poet who wrote it?*

1 All losses are restored.	( )	Carroll
2 Fled is that music.	( )	Coleridge
3 Go, mark him well.	( )	Fitzgerald
4 He went galumphing back.	( )	Hunt
5 I blessed them unaware.	( )	Keats
6 It might have been.	( )	Kipling
7 I've taken my fun.	( )	Lear
8 Letters squirmed like snakes.	( )	Longfellow
9 Make me thy lyre.	( )	Lowell
10 My heart is pure.	( )	Milton
11 Of thee I sing.	( )	Poe
12 Say I'm growing old.	( )	Scott
13 Ten thousand saw I.	( )	Shakespeare
14 The devil take her!	( )	Shelley
15 The moon never beams.	( )	Smith
16 The Moving Finger writes.	( )	Southey
17 They dined on mince.	( )	Suckling
18 'Twas a famous victory.	( )	Tennyson
19 Where were ye, Nymphs?	( )	Whittier
20 You know the rest.	( )	Wordsworth

28 · Doctors in Literature. *The medical profession, like the clergy and the military, is exceedingly well represented in the world of literature. Briefly described here are ten of its outstanding members. Can you recognize them and name their creators?*

1 With a box of jewels and the able assistance of Mephistopheles, this Renaissance scholar won the affections of a pure and simple young girl.

2 For every ailment this Spanish physician prescribed plenty of warm water and bleeding.

3 As ship's surgeon aboard the *Antelope*, the *Adventure*, and the *Hopewell*, he travelled to some very unusual countries.

4 A medical student at the University of Ingolstadt, he constructed a man out of some odds and ends of cadavers and endowed him with life by using a spark of lightning.

5 Eighteen years in the Bastille with nothing but cobbling to do to pass the time had considerably damaged this doctor's mind.

6 This doctor had to choose between saving the life of a good but ordinary man and an artistic genius who was a scoundrel.

7 Fond of experiments, this elderly doctor persuaded four of his contemporaries to drink some water from the Fountain of Youth.

8 Swallowing a compound of his own prescription transformed this eminently respectable physician into a deformed and evil fiend.

9 Wounded in the shoulder (or was it the leg?) during the battle of Maiwand, he was invalided home to London, where he took lodgings in Baker Street.

10 Discoverer of an organism that preys on bacteria, he had an opportunity to test it when the plague broke out in a West Indies island.

29 · Characters Concerned with Bridges. *The ten characters in this quiz were more or less concerned with bridges. Can you identify them as well as the stories in which they appeared?*

1 With the help of two companions, this hero held an invading army at bay at the far end of a bridge while the near end was being cut away.

2 Fighting with the Spanish Loyalists, this American successfully blew up a strategic bridge but lost his life as a consequence.

3 About to be hanged by Union soldiers from a railroad bridge over an Alabama creek, this Southerner imagined for a moment that he had escaped.

4 Seeing five persons fall to their death when a suspension bridge broke as they were crossing gave this Franciscan monk an opportunity to make theology an exact science by finding out why they were doomed to die at that moment.

5 This famous traveller was a passenger on a train that just managed to cross a disintegrating suspension bridge by going at 100 miles an hour.

6 In a snowstorm this little girl wandered halfway across a bridge and then fell off.

7 A freshly chipped place on the side of a stone bridge was the clue that enabled this sleuth to deduce that a supposed murder was really suicide.

8 At midnight on London Bridge this girl met and gave necessary information to some people who were trying to establish the identity of an orphan they had befriended.

9 When this famous outlaw met a tall stranger in the middle of a narrow foot-bridge they fought with clubs for the right of way until the outlaw was knocked into the creek.

10 On a plank bridge over a small stream this circus equestrian and his fellow workers fought off some tough members of a rival circus who were bent on destruction.

30 · Money in Literature. *Money may not be everything, but the sums involved in the stories briefly sketched below were very important to the characters concerned. Can you identify both story and character?*

1 He borrowed 3,000 ducats from an enemy to lend to a friend, and nearly lost his life when he was unable to pay it back in three months.

2 For 1,000 guilders he agreed to rid a town of rats.

3 This linen weaver was robbed one winter night of his life savings, £272 12s. 6d.

4 His financial philosophy was as follows: 'Annual income twenty pounds, annual expenditure nineteen nineteen six, result happiness. Annual income twenty pounds, annual expenditure twenty pounds ought and six, result misery.'

5 Christmas was coming and she wanted to buy her husband a present, but all the money she had was one dollar and eighty-seven cents.

6 As soon as she could earn twelve pounds with which to buy a typewriter she left her too-successful husband.

7 Through Indian magic he was granted three wishes: the first was for £200, which he received the next day from an insurance company as compensation for his son's accidental death.

8 He spent 36,000 francs to replace a lost necklace worth only 500.

9 Through an agent, this Hawaiian bought for two centimes a bottle which would provide wealth and riches for its owner while he lived and eternal damnation after he died, and which could only be sold at a loss.

10 In order to inherit seven million dollars he had to spend one million within a year and have nothing to show for it.

31 · Some Interrupted Weddings. *Weddings aren't always the happy events that they are planned to be, as the ten fictional incidents herewith will show. Do you remember the stories and the authors who wrote them?*

1 To avoid her marriage the next day to a man of her father's choice, our youthful heroine—married secretly to another only a few days before—took a potion that put her in a death-like trance for forty-two hours.

2 The first time our hero tried to get married the banns were forbidden by a stranger who made a living by doing such things in order to extract money from the groom; the second time he was arrested at the altar on orders of his father, who opposed the union.

3 Fulfilling the threat that he should be with his creator on the latter's wedding night, a monster appeared and strangled the bride.

4 As a governess and her employer stood before the altar, a stranger interrupted the wedding service by asserting that the groom-to-be was already married and that his wife was still living.

5 The wedding reception was abruptly terminated when an uninvited guest appeared, danced the bride around to the doorway, threw her on his horse, and galloped away.

6 The parson had just pronounced them man and wife, and, as the groom turned to kiss the bride, a shot rang out and she collapsed in his arms.

7 An English nobleman was so annoyed when his American bride disappeared immediately after their wedding that he appealed to a famous consulting detective for aid.

8 At twenty minutes to nine a bride-to-be received a note from her fiancé which cancelled the wedding, and she never afterwards looked upon the light of day.

9 Being congenital rubbernecks, this couple simply could not resist the urge to join the crowd of sidewalk superintendents that had gathered outside the church where their wedding was to take place.

10 This was the note that Obadiah Binks sent to the girl who was waiting at the church: 'I can't get away to marry you today. My wife won't let me.'

32 · First Lines of Famous Poems. *Here are the first lines of twenty well-known poems. Can you identify each poem and name the poet who wrote it?*

1 A gentle knight was pricking on the plaine. . . .
2 Blessings on thee, little man!
3 Bowed by the weight of centuries he leans. . . .
4 Come live with me and be my love. . . .
5 Descend, ye Nine! descend and sing!
6 Earth has not anything to show more fair. . . .
7 Goodbye, proud world! I'm going home. . . .
8 Hence, vain deluding Joys. . . .
9 Here's to the maiden of bashful fifteen. . . .
10 I have had playmates, I have had companions. . . .
11 I met a traveller from an antique land. . . .
12 It was many and many a year ago. . . .
13 It was roses, roses, all the way. . . .
14 Jenny kissed me when we met. . . .
15 Much have I travelled in the realms of gold. . . .
16 Sweet Auburn! loveliest village of the plain. . . .
17 Tears, idle tears, I know not what they mean. . . .
18 Tell me not, sweet, I am unkind. . . .
19 The Assyrian came down like a wolf on the fold. . . .
20 Why so pale and wan, fond lover?

33 · Who is She? *In the quotations from well-known poems that are listed below, can you identify the 'she' in each?*

1 'Adieu!' she cries; and waved her lily hand.

2 Alone she cuts and binds the grain,
And sings a melancholy strain.

3 And still she slept an azure-lidded sleep,
In blanchèd linen, smooth, and lavendered.

4 Her arms across her breast she laid;
She was more fair than words can say.

5 Her gentle limbs she did undress, and lay down in her loveliness.

6 'Let spades be trumps!' she said, and trumps they were.

7 She dwelt among the untrodden ways beside the springs of Dove.

8 She excels each mortal thing upon the dull earth dwelling.

9 She found me roots of relish sweet, and honey wild, and manna dew.

10 She had a heart—how shall I say?—too soon made glad.

11 She had three lilies in her hand, and the stars in her hair were seven.

12 'She'll very well pass for forty-three
In the dusk, with a light behind her!'

13 She looked down to blush, and she looked up to sigh,
With a smile on her lips, and a tear in her eye.

14 She put my arms about her waist, and made her smooth white shoulder bare, and all her yellow hair displaced.

15 She said, 'I am aweary, aweary, I would that I were dead!'

16 She stood breast high among the corn,
Clasped by the golden light of morn.

17 She stooped where the cool spring bubbled up
And filled for him her small tin cup.

18 Then the maiden clasped her hands and prayed
That savèd she might be.

19 This maiden she lived with no other thought than to love and be loved by me.

20 Would you know how first he met her? She was cutting bread and butter.

34 · Twice-married Men. *Briefly described below are ten heroes of fiction who were married twice. Can you identify them and name the author who created them?*

1 After his first wife divorced him, he married the girl he had first encountered behind a perfume counter at Saks'.

2 This doctor's first wife was a student nurse, his second a wealthy society woman who married him because of his growing fame.

3 As a young law clerk, he married the boss's daughter; in later years he married a childhood friend, also a lawyer's daughter.

4 After an unfortunate alliance with a dissolute dipsomaniac, he found happiness by marrying his ward's governess.

5 His first marriage was with an English widow whom he had known as a child; his second was with a Spanish widow whom he had courted as a young man.

6 After his first wife eloped with an unprincipled adventurer and was later reported dead, this wealthy landowner married the daughter of the local judge.

7 Tricked into a marriage with a barmaid in a near-by town, this eldest son of the village squire was relieved when her sudden death enabled him to marry the daughter of a neighbouring farmer.

8 This stuffy businessman was surprised when his first wife left him to make her own living as a typist, but he soon married another, more amenable woman.

9 Following his first wife's death, he married a young woman with a chequered past, in the futile hope that his name would give her a secure social standing.

10 When his first wife fell in love with the architect who was building their house and left him, this man of property got a divorce twelve years later in order to marry a young French girl.

35 · Unusual Hiding Places. *This quiz brings to your attention some interesting hiding places that were either used by or discovered by well-known literary figures. From the descriptions below can you recall the stories and the characters concerned?*

1 Under a couple of loose bricks in the floor this miser hid two leather bags full of gold coins.

2 Having killed and robbed a Yankee soldier, this resourceful heroine hid his wallet in a baby's diaper.

3 Among other souvenirs that she hid in a secret drawer of her desk lest her husband get curious was a £1,000 bank note given to her by a wealthy admirer.

4 A political intriguer baffled the police by hiding a letter in its own envelope turned inside out, but this amateur detective found it with ease.

5 With the police hot on his trail, a thief popped a stolen jewel into one of the six plaster busts of Napoleon he was moulding, from which this celebrated sleuth extracted it some time later.

6 Not knowing what it was but wishing to keep it handy to use as a nut cracker, this boy hid the Royal Seal of England in a suit of armour on the wall.

7 After her brothers had killed her boy friend and buried him in a forest, she dug up his body, cut off his head, and hid it in a pot of basil.

8 In a drunken stupor this Yankee sailor hid a bottle of port in the arms of a statue of the Virgin. Some time later, when the statue was being set up in a church, the bottle broke, and the wine, oozing through drop by drop, was mistaken for a miracle.

9 To prevent the incrimination of the gentleman she loved in the theft of a valuable jewel, this servant girl hid his paint-stained nightgown in a spot of quicksand.

10 After recovering from a prolonged binge, this dipsomaniac prepared for the next one by hiding two pints of whisky in the toilet, suspending two pints on strings outside his bedroom window, and putting one behind the books in the bookcase.

36 · 'The Face is Familiar. . . .' *Everyone is familiar with these twenty-five well-known titles, each of which is a description of the main character of the story. But remembering the names of the characters is something else. Can you match up each title with the proper character?*

1 BARRIE: *The Little Minister*   ( ) Antonio
2 CATHER: *A Lost Lady*   ( ) Jody Baxter
3 COLLINS: *The Woman in White*   ( ) Natty Bumppo
4 CONRAD: *The Nigger of the Narcissus*   ( ) Anne Catherick
5 COOPER: *The Deerslayer*   ( ) Edmond Dantes
6 DE LA ROCHE: *The Master of Jalna*   ( ) Gavin Dishart
7 DICKENS: *Our Mutual Friend*   ( ) Ellen Douglas
8 DUMAS: *The Count of Monte Cristo*   ( ) Daniel Dravot
9 GALSWORTHY: *The Man of Property*   ( ) Marian Forrester
10 GOLDSMITH: *The Vicar of Wakefield*   ( ) Soames Forsyte
11 HALE: *The Man Without a Country*   ( ) George Fotheringay
12 HARDY: *The Mayor of Casterbridge*   ( ) John Harmon
13 O. HENRY: *The Gentle Grafter*   ( ) Clem Hawley
14 HOPE: *The Prisoner of Zenda*   ( ) Michael Henchard
15 HUGO: *The Hunchback of Notre Dame*   ( ) Hank Morgan
16 KAUFMAN-HART: *The Man Who Came
        to Dinner*   ( ) Philip Nolan
17 KIPLING: *The Man Who Would be
        King*   ( ) Jeff Peters
18 KNIGHT: *The Flying Yorkshireman*   ( ) Daniel Pike
19 MARQUIS: *The Old Soak*   ( ) Charles Primrose
20 RAWLINGS: *The Yearling*   ( ) Quasimodo
21 SCOTT: *The Lady of the Lake*   ( ) Rudolph
22 SHAKESPEARE: *The Merchant of Venice*   ( ) Sam Small
23 TARKINGTON: *The Man from Home*   ( ) James Wait
24 TWAIN: *The Connecticut Yankee*   ( ) Renny Whiteoak
25 WELLS: *The Man Who Could Work
        Miracles*   ( ) Sheridan Whiteside

37 · Familiar Lines of Famous Poems. *Quoted below are the first two words of twenty-five familiar lines of poetry. Can you complete them and name the poets?*

1 Ah, make . . . .
2 Blessings on . . . .
3 Breathes there . . . .
4 Bright star! . . . .
5 Come live . . . .
6 Descend, ye . . . .
7 Far from . . . .
8 Flow gently . . . .
9 Full fathom . . . .
10 Great rats . . . .
11 How doth . . . .
12 In Xanadu . . . .
13 I wandered . . . .
14 Little Lamb . . . .
15 My strength . . . .
16 Once upon . . . .
17 O wild . . . .
18 She walks . . . .
19 The blessed . . . .
20 'Twas brillig . . . .
21 'Twas many . . . .
22 Whan that . . . .
23 Whenas in . . . .
24 When lilacs . . . .
25 With fingers . . . .

38 · Transportation in Fiction. *There have been many famous travellers in literature, and some of them have used extremely unusual methods of transportation. From the descriptions given here can you recall the names of the travellers and the stories in which they appeared?*

1 Fastened to the claw of a huge bird, this famous sailor was carried to a valley of diamonds.

2 He travelled about in a boat pulled by a swan.

3 By fastening bird feathers to their shoulders with wax, this father and son managed to fly from their prison.

4 Their heads are green and their hands are blue and they went to sea in a sieve.

5 By saying, 'Abracadabra, dum, dum, dum,' the crippled owner of a magic travelling cloak was able to float through the air with the greatest of ease.

6 On a snow sledge equipped with sails, this world traveller went 200 miles from Fort Kearney to Omaha in five hours.

7 This little boy, on being swallowed by a dog-fish as big as a five-storied house, discovered that his father had been living quite comfortably in the fish's stomach for two years.

8 This trio of herring-fishers went out to sea in a wooden shoe.

9 She went to a ball in a coach made from a pumpkin.

10 While confined in a huge bird-cage which had been remodelled into a living-room, he was carried out to sea by a huge eagle and dropped 200 leagues from shore.

39 · Alice in Wonderland. *We suggest that you first take time off and re-read* Alice in Wonderland *and* Through the Looking Glass. *But if you try the quiz first, the chances are you'll re-read those delightful volumes anyway, so either way you win! Here, then, are twenty unforgettable speeches by various characters in the stories. Can you remember who said them?*

1 Curiouser and curiouser!

2 *Everybody* has won, and *all* must have prizes.

3 It was the *best* butter.

4 Off with their heads!

5 Everything's got a moral, if you can only find it.

6 I only took the regular course. . . . the different branches of Arithmetic—Ambition, Distraction, Uglification, and Derision.

7 No! No! Sentence first—verdict afterwards.

8 In most gardens they make the beds too soft—so that the flowers are always asleep.

9 A slow sort of country! Now, *here*, you see, it takes all the running you can do to keep in the same place.

10 What's the use of their having names if they won't answer to them?

11 If you think we're wax-works, you ought to pay, you know. Wax-works weren't made to be looked at for nothing. Nohow!

12 The time has come . . . to talk of many things: of shoes—and ships—and sealing wax—of cabbages—and kings.

13 The rule is, jam tomorrow and jam yesterday—but never jam *today*.

14 Why, sometimes I've believed as many as six impossible things before breakfast.

15 When I use a word, it means just what I choose it to mean— neither more nor less.

16 A minute goes by so fearfully quick. You might as well try to stop a Bandersnatch!

17 It's as large as life, and twice as natural!

18 Well, now that we have seen each other, if you'll believe in me, I'll believe in you. Is that a bargain?

19 It's my own invention.

20 Always speak the truth—think before you speak—and write it down afterwards.

40 · Songs and their Singers. *Each of the characters in this quiz is closely associated with a particular song. Can you identify the singers and name the stories in which they appeared?*

1 Every time he came home, this singing waiter would start warbling *Molly Malone* as he came up the stairs, while his wife would try to get the door opened before he finished the verse.

2 This retired pirate was fond of roaring out an old sea-chanty that began: 'Fifteen men on the dead man's chest—Yo-ho-ho and a bottle of rum!'

3 This young lover sang a Provençal ditty by the couch of a young lady who was fast asleep.

4 Never once hitting the right note, this tone-deaf artist's model sought to entertain her new acquaintances with a horrible rendering of *Ben Bolt*.

5 To a tune of his own invention he sang a song variously titled *Haddock's Eyes*, *The Aged Aged Man*, *Ways and Means*, and *A-sitting On A Gate*.

6 When the prima donna failed to appear, this guest acted as a substitute and not only electrified the audience but also won the love of the hero by singing *The Rosary*.

7 This idle lout composed and sang a song called *The Three Pigeons* in honour of the tavern in which he spent most of his time.

8 On her annual holiday from the silk factory she wandered around carolling 'God's in his heaven, all's right with the world!' and other tunes which influenced her listeners.

9 This invisible spirit lured along a shipwreck victim by singing: 'Full fathom five thy father lies.'

10 To cheer up her old father she sang a melancholy song that he was fond of, called *When Lovely Woman Stoops to Folly*.

41 · **A Patchwork Poem.** *The following effusion, technically known as a canto, consists of twenty lines from well-known poems. Can you name the author and the poem from which each line was taken?*

1 I wandered lonely as a cloud.
2 Where danced the moon on Monan's rill;
3 It was many and many a year ago:
4 The night birds all that hour were still.
5 When first she gleamed upon my sight
6 (A perfect woman, nobly planned!)
7 Her hair was long, her foot was light;
8 She had three lilies in her hand,
9 A nest of robins in her hair,
10 A general flavour of mild decay;
11 She was as good as she was fair—
12 She was more fair than words can say.
13 That brave vibration each way free
14 Seemed to have known a better day.
15 How sweet and fair she seemed to be!
16 (O frabjous day! Callooh! Callay!)
17 'Tis better to have loved and lost,
18 But this alone I know full well:
19 She's all my fancy painted her,
20 A sight to dream of, not to tell!

42 · **Statues in Literature.** *This quiz concerns famous statues in song and story. Can you name the stories and their authors?*

1 The night before a dictator's assassination, his wife dreamed that she saw his statue spouting blood from a hundred places.

2 Because a soldier held an invading army at bay and saved Rome, the City Fathers erected a statue of him in the public square.

3 When a juggler, paying the only tribute within his power, juggled six copper balls and a dozen knives before the image of the Virgin, the statue came to life and wiped his streaming brow.

4 The wax figure of a man who had killed fourteen wives by tickling the soles of their feet as they slept had his fingers curled, as if in the act of tickling, and one eye closed in a wink.

5 A statue erected to a murdered man accepts an invitation to dine with the murderer.

6 All that remains of the statue of a king of kings is the pedestal, two vast and trunkless legs, and the head half-buried in the desert sand.

7 Wine from a broken bottle cradled in the arms of a terra cotta Madonna seeped through, causing it to 'bleed' and creating a miracle.

8 Because a practical joker switched the labels, a huge statue of Hercules is delivered in a packing box instead of the corpse in a barrel that was expected.

9 One of the many artists who had been the lover of an ageless courtesan used her as a model for a statuette which became a popular household decoration throughout France.

10 While revisiting the old school to dedicate a statue to an empire builder, a bishop accidentally takes a nerve tonic designed for timid elephants, and under its influence sneaks out at night and paints the statue pink.

43 · Elopers in Literature. *Briefly described below are some famous elopements from the pages of literature. Can you identify either of the persons concerned in each affair and name the story in which they appeared?*

1 Before running off with her Christian lover, this beautiful Jewess helped herself to a liberal supply of her father's money and jewels.

2 This clergyman's daughter was kidnapped without much resistance by a noble suitor who went through what he thought was a mock marriage ceremony, only to find out later that it was legal.

3 Pursued by her angry father, this runaway girl and her Highland chieftain were compelled to cross a storm-lashed lake and were drowned before his eyes.

4 This bold lover crept into his enemy's castle, wooed and won the daughter of the house, and fled away with her into a January storm.

5 While dancing with the bride at a wedding reception, this gallant manoeuvred her towards the door, swung her up onto his horse, and dashed away with her.

6 Her father and her three brothers were killed in the feud that flared up when this Southern belle eloped with a son of the rival family.

7 Despite his family's disapproval, this soldier eloped with the penniless girl to whom he had been betrothed since childhood, whereupon his father obliterated his name from the family Bible.

8 Her parents and four sisters were considerably upset when this frivolous girl ran off to London with a militia officer, but felt a little better when the elopers were married a few days later.

9 On the evening of her wedding to her cousin, she yielded to the blandishments of a wealthy aristocrat and ran off with him, only to have him suggest some months later that she marry his valet.

10 The daughter of a highly respectable draper, she eloped to Paris with a travelling salesman who had inherited £12,000.

44 · Criminals in Literature. *Not all the criminals in literature are to be found in detective fiction. Here are ten well-known characters who were guilty of various crimes other than murder. Can you identify each one and name the story in which he appears?*

1 To prevent the coronation of the King of Ruritania, this half-brother gave him a bottle of drugged wine and then kidnapped him.

2 When this Chinese boy and his father discovered that a delicious repast resulted from burning down their dwelling, they became habitual incendiaries.

3 This U.S. naval officer was convicted of treason in connection with the Aaron Burr conspiracy and was exiled for 57 years.

4 Convicted of adultery, she was forced to wear a scarlet 'A' on her dress at all times.

5 Daily practice enabled him to become the most proficient one of a gang of boys who pilfered handkerchiefs from unsuspecting victims.

6 Always ethical, he never swindled a Midwestern farmer without giving him at least a gold brick or some phony stock certificates to show for his money.

7 This one-legged sea-cook led a mutiny aboard the schooner *Hispaniola*.

8 For duelling in the streets, he was exiled by the Prince of Verona.

9 Condemned to death for flirting, he was reprieved when the emperor appointed him Lord High Executioner.

10 On the spur of the moment he stole the life savings of the village weaver.

45 · Characters who had Unusual Powers. 'Faster than a speeding bullet! More powerful than a locomotive! Able to leap over the highest building at a single bound! It's SUPERMAN!!!' *That gentle reader, is what it takes to be today's No. 1 hero of the comic magazines. On a somewhat different plane the world of books has its supermen, too. From these brief descriptions of their extraordinary powers can you identify them and name the stories in which they appeared?*

1 Gazing out of an upper storey window, an unwilling guest was horrified to see his host emerge from a lower window and crawl head first down the wall of his towering castle.

2 Entering the hero's room in the guise of a poodle, he vanished in a puff of smoke and re-appeared as the villain of the piece.

3 She lived in a South American forest and spoke to the birds in their own language.

4 Every night for twenty-five years, by 'dreaming true', this convict and his sweetheart met in their dreams and re-lived every pleasurable event that either had ever experienced.

5 Because her scientist-father brought her up on poisons, she was immune to them, although her breathing would kill insects and wither flowers.

6 A split personality to begin with, this doctor succeeded with the aid of certain drugs in splitting it completely.

7 A sermon on Faith, by Sister Minnie Tekel Upharsin Smith, of California, convinced this Yorkshire inventor that he could fly like a bird—and he did!

8 A placid disposition and a calm philosophy, aided by a most unusual climate, enabled this monastery head to live for 250 years.

9 By sheer will-power he upset a bar-room lamp and then progressed through a series of miracles climaxed by stopping the rotation of the earth.

10 He paddled and steered his own canoe by mental telepathy.

46 · Famous Soldiers. *The pages of literature are liberally dotted with soldiers of many armies and from many wars. Of the ten briefly described below, can you name each, as well as the author who created him?*

1 In matters vegetable, animal, and mineral, he was the very model of a modern major-general.

2 Leaving his unhappy bride of six weeks, this English captain went off to war and was killed in the Battle of Waterloo.

3 Wounded in the groin at the siege of Namur, this old soldier, after his recovery, reconstructed the battlefield's terrain in miniature.

4 This soldier was a soldier bold, and used to war's alarms; but a cannon ball took off his legs, so he laid down his arms.

5 Captured by the Russians during the Crimean War, this lieutenant found his way back, after thirty years in Siberia, to the English army post in Khyber Pass.

6 During the early years of the War Between the States he made a fortune as a blockade runner, finally enlisting in the Confederate army after the fall of Atlanta.

7 This unsophisticated country boy had fretted for weeks to be in action against the Confederate army, but when his first battle came along he turned and ran.

8 As head of the American military government in an Italian town, he did everything he could to make the citizens happy, even to securing them a new village bell.

9 '*Courage, mon ami! le diable est mort!*' was the oft repeated motto of this Burgundian soldier.

10 Because he shot a sleeping comrade, this British soldier was hanged in the presence of his regiment.

47 · Numbers in Titles. *The numbers which go to make up the titles of the books listed below have been omitted. Can you fill in the blanks?*

a. ....*Men on a Horse,* by ABBOT and HOLM
b. ....*Years at Hull House,* by JANE ADDAMS
c. ....*Cousins,* by LOUISA M. ALCOTT
d. ....*That Were Hanged,* by LEONID ANDREYEV
e. ....*Pound Look,* by JAMES M. BARRIE
f. ....*Who Fled,* by FREDERIC PROKOSCH
g. ....*Steps,* by JOHN BUCHAN
h. ....*Years Before the Mast,* by RICHARD H. DANA
i. ....by JOHN DOS PASSOS
j. ....*Years After,* by ALEXANDRE DUMAS
k. ....*Black Pennys,* by JOSEPH HERGESHEIMER
l. ....*Men in a Boat,* by JEROME K. JEROME
m. ....*Years in Sing Sing,* by LEWIS E. LAWES
n. ....*Pillars of Wisdom,* by T. E. LAWRENCE
o. ....*Characters in Search of an Author,* by PIRANDELLO
p. ....*Days That Shook the World,* by JOHN REED
q. ....*Gentlemen of Verona,* by WILLIAM SHAKESPEARE
r. ....*Pound Bank Note,* by MARK TWAIN
s. ....*Leagues Under the Sea,* by JULES VERNE
t. ....*Days of Musa Dagh,* by FRANZ WERFEL

48 · Lines that Precede Famous Lines. *Quoted below are lines from twenty well-known poems which have the distinction of immediately preceding lines that are familiar to all. Can you quote the lines that follow these?*

1 What I aspired to be, and was not, comforts me.

2 My Mary's asleep by thy murmuring stream.

3 Did ye not hear it?—No; 'twas but the wind,
   Or the car rattling o'er the stony street.

4 He went like one that hath been stunned, and is of sense forlorn.

5 But I was desolate and sick of an old passion
   When I awoke and found the dawn was gray.

6 Some for the Glories of This World; and some
   Sigh for the Prophet's Paradise to come.

7 Truth from his lips prevailed with double sway.

8 All that beauty, all that wealth e'er gave
   Awaits alike the inevitable hour.

9 It matters not how strait the gate,
   How charged with punishments the scroll.

10 Say I'm weary, say I'm sad,
   Say that health and wealth have missed me.

11 They've taken all his buttons off an' cut his stripes away.

12 Hang a lantern aloft in the belfry arch
   Of the North Church tower as a signal light.

13 Thousands at his bidding speed,
   And post o'er land and ocean without rest.

14 Look for me by moonlight, watch for me by moonlight.

15 Know then thyself, presume not God to scan.

16 She is won! we are gone, over bank, bush, and scaur!

17 Shall I compare thee to a summer's day?

18 Our sincerest laughter with some pain is fraught.

19 'Why, that I cannot tell,' said he.

20 In the spring a livelier iris changes on the burnished dove.

49 · A Mother Goose Quiz. *Presumably everyone is well acquainted with the childhood verses generally known as the Mother Goose nursery rhymes. So, just to check up on your memory, here is a refresher quiz.*

1 Who put pussy in the well?

2 What musical instrument did Mother Hubbard's dog play?

3 What was the occupation of Little Tommy Tittlemouse?

4 For what did Simple Simon fish in his mother's pail?

5 What was the nationality of Taffy, notorious thief of beef and marrow bones?

6 What remedy did Jack apply when he tumbled down hill and broke his crown?

7 Who was urged, in a proposal, to sit on a cushion and sew a fine seam?

8 What did Wee Willie Winkie wear?

9 What frightened Miss Muffet?

10 What did the old woman who lived in a shoe feed to her many children?

11 When old King Cole called his fiddlers three, how did they reply?

12 What happened to the bag pudding that King Arthur and his queen were unable to finish?

13 On what day of the week did Solomon Grundy die?

14 What did the Knave of Hearts steal?

15 How many hairs will make a wig?

16 What gastronomical enticement did Robin Redbreast offer to Jenny Wren?

17 What penalty was given to the three little kittens who lost their mittens?

18 Where did Bobby Shaftoe go?

19 What was stolen by Tom, the piper's son?

20 What time does the ten o'clock scholar arrive?

50 · Ten Famous Detectives. *Even if you're not a detective-story addict, you can probably identify the supersleuths who are briefly described below and name their creators.*

1 The very first of a long line of fiction detectives, he lived by candlelight during the day and wandered the streets of Paris by night.

2 A little, round-faced Catholic priest, he is forever carrying an umbrella.

3 Among the hobbies of this famous detective were violin playing, indoor pistol practice, and taking dope.

4 A member of the Honolulu police force, this Chinese detective lives on Punchbowl Hill and has eleven children.

5 A wealthy dilettante, he used the extensive knowledge of modern art, chess, Egyptology, poker, dogs, dragons, and psychology to solve several of New York's celebrated crimes, and he smoked Regie cigarettes.

6 A former member of the Belgian police, he is proud of his vegetable marrows, his luxuriant moustache, and his 'little grey cells'.

7 His ambition was to retire from the British police force and raise roses on his farm.

8 An expert on first editions, fine wines, early music, and cricket, this charming English aristocrat married the woman whom he freed of a murder charge.

9 A huge man, he is fond of orchids and of beer in large quantities.

10 He drives a Dusenberg, collects first editions, and has a father who takes snuff.

51 · Place Names in Poetry. *Each of the thirty place names listed below, some of which are real and some imaginary, is closely, if not uniquely, associated with a particular poet. After making the mental jump of identifying the poem in which the place name appears, can you name the poet?*

1 Afton	11 Gulliby Isles	21 Southwerk
2 Auburn	12 Hamelin	22 Spoon River
3 Azores	13 Kew	23 Suwanee
4 Blenheim	14 Ludlow	24 Tara
5 Chillon	15 Moulmein	25 Tilbury Town
6 Congo	16 Naishápúr	26 Titipu
7 Dove	17 Oxus	27 Ware
8 Gitche Gumee	18 Reading	28 Xanadu
9 Glenartney	19 Samarkand	29 Yaanek
10 Göttingen	20 Shalott	30 Zemmery Fidd

52 · Shakespeare's Opening Lines. *How well do you know your Shakespeare? Quoted below are the opening lines of ten of his plays. Can you name the plays and tell who speaks the lines?*

1 In sooth, I know not why I am so sad:
   It wearies me; you say it wearies you.

2 When shall we three meet again
   In thunder, lightning, or in rain?

3 Hence! home, you idle creatures, get you home:
   Is this a holiday?

4 If music be the food of love, play on,
   Give me excess of it; that, surfeiting,
   The appetite may sicken and so die.

5 Now, fair Hippolyta, our nuptial hour
   Draws on apace.

6 I thought the king had more affected the Duke of Albany than
   Cornwall.

7 Now is the winter of our discontent
   Made glorious summer by this sun of York.

8 So shaken as we are, so wan with care,
   Find we a time for frighted peace to pant.

9 Let fame, that all hunt after in their lives,
   Live register'd upon our brazen tombs,
   And then grace us in the disgrace of death.

10 Hung be the heavens with black, yield day to night!
   Comets, importing change of time and states,
   Brandish your crystal tresses in the sky.

53 Characters who Were Shipwrecked. *The literary figures in this quiz have one thing in common: they have all been involved in shipwrecks. From the brief description of their experiences as given below can you identify them and name the authors who created them?*

1 After sixteen lonely years on the Island of Despair, this castaway was shocked to come upon the imprint of a naked foot in the middle of a sandy beach.

2 Returning home after eleven years as a castaway on a tropical isle, he discovered that his wife had married their childhood friend.

3 After swimming ashore following the wreck of the *Antelope*, this ship's surgeon fell asleep exhausted and awoke to find himself the prisoner of a race of tiny people.

4 Shipwrecked while on a trip from Cadiz to Leghorn, this exiled Spanish grandee finally swam to the shore of an Aegean island where he was comforted by a beautiful seventeen-year-old girl.

5 Set adrift by his brother in an open boat with an infant daughter and a set of books on magic, he landed on an island and in the ensuing years learned magic so well that he was able to create a storm which wrecked his brother's ship.

6 When the yacht of an aristocratic family was wrecked near a desert island, this butler became master of the small community—until they were rescued some time later.

7 He was the only survivor of an ill-fated whaling expedition.

8 The sole survivor when the *Piccadilly Daisy* sank, he lived on toasted lizards, prickly pears, and parrot gizzards.

9 Mutineers scuttled the ship off the coast of Florida and left to their fate this second officer and the beautiful young girl whom he had taken off a derelict, but they were eventually rescued from their lifeboat.

10 Bound for Bankok in the barque *Judea*, this youthful second mate survived a hurricane, a fire, and an explosion, and eventually arrived in command of a rowing boat.

54 · Poets in Literature. *Poets are people, too, and as such they frequently appear as characters in the pages of literature. Can you identify the ten that are briefly sketched below and name the stories in which they appeared?*

1 Crowds of love-sick maidens followed this long-haired poet around (not that he objected) but he loved only the village milkmaid.

2 He wrote passionate lyrics to his lady love and hung them on the trees in the forest of Arden.

3 After his death this Spoon River poet realized that he had passed by the real material of poetry which lay all around him in favour of artificial forms and trite ideas.

4 Although he thought it very vulgar to break into print, he had visions of seeing his love elegies 'on a beautiful quarto page, where a neat rivulet of text should meander through a meadow of margin'.

5 This Canadian poet died just as his book, *Last Poems*, was published; and a copy of it was buried with him.

6 This young man wrote what he did not doubt was poetry to a young lady whose principal charm was speaking in baby talk.

7 This eighteen-year-old poet read sonnets to the thirty-five-year-old clergyman's wife with whom he was in love.

8 She was the author of *Ode to an Expiring Frog*, which she recited at the public breakfasts she gave for celebrities.

9 Before she died at fourteen, this girl kept a scrapbook of obituaries, accidents, and cases of patient suffering clipped from the *Presbyterian Observer* and made up elegiac tributes to the unfortunate victims.

10 After his reincarnation as a cockroach, this poet wrote *vers libre* on a typewriter whose keys he operated by diving on them head first.

55 · Famous Ghost Stories. *Not every spook gives rise to goose flesh, as these brief summaries of ten well-known ghost stories will prove. Can you recall the title and author of each?*

1 'You may be an undigested bit of beef, a blot of mustard, a crumb of cheese, a fragment of underdone potatoe,' scoffed the unbeliever when the ghost of his former business partner appeared.

2 He was haunted not only by the ghost of the woman he had ceased to love but also by the ghosts of the vehicle in which she had travelled and her four attendants.

3 Immediately after her death, this woman appeared at the home of an old friend and spent most of an hour and forty-five minutes praising Drelincourt's '*The Christian's Defence against the Fear of Death*.'

4 This unfortunate writer was haunted by the ghosts of his two wives.

5 After she had been killed in a motor accident, this charming Bohemian gave a new slant on life to the stodgy and conventional banker who had purchased her car by spending a summer vacation with him.

6 Despite the efforts of their governess, two young children were evilly influenced by the ghosts of their former governess and their father's ex-valet.

7 His father's ghost informed a prince of how he had been poisoned in his sleep and pleaded with him to revenge his foul and most unnatural murder.

8 After his fruitless search for a lost girl friend, her spirit came to him in a shabbily furnished room as an unmistakable odour of mignonette.

9 Ineffective and unsuccessful all his life, he proved to be a failure as a ghost too, for he not only failed to scare anybody but he also forgot how to return to the Beyond.

10 With *Pinkerton's Champion Stain Remover and Paragon Detergent* an unsentimental American removed a blood stain that had been on an English castle floor for 300 years, and this ghost had to renew it every night with watercolours.

56 · Fiction's Famous Funerals. *Briefly described below are ten memorable funerals from the pages of literature. Can you remember the characters concerned and the stories in which they appeared?*

1 Amid much pomp and circumstance, this valet was buried in Westminster Abbey while the nation mourned the 'death' of his employer, a famous artist.

2 With two of his companions, this boy attended the funeral services being held for them in the belief that they had been drowned.

3 This detective interrupted a funeral and opened the coffin just in time to remove a woman who had been chloroformed and put in with the corpse.

4 This old lady had her first automobile ride, in a hearse at the age of 101.

5 Every time these two old ladies poisoned a man they buried him in the cellar with complete funeral services and full mourning.

6 This dead soldier was given a 'Viking funeral' by his younger brother, after the manner of a game they used to play in childhood.

7 While her own funeral was going on, this girl sat at one side and discussed it with her dead mother-in-law and other newly deceased members of the community.

8 Because he had insisted on cremation, this man's partner carried his frozen corpse around until he found a derelict ship, built a roaring fire in the boiler, and stuffed in the remains.

9 Within a few hours after this unemployed singing waiter died, an undertaker appeared and offered a funeral at a price a few dollars less than the amount of his insurance policy.

10 As part of a sales talk to induce this repulsive misanthrope to hang himself, the beauties of his funeral were graphically pictured: friends weeping and wailing for miles around and saying nice things about him that they never said in his lifetime.

57 · Twenty Famous Pen Names. *In the column on the left are twenty pen names that are famous in literature. Can you match them up with the real names of the writers in the column on the right?*

1 Currer Bell	( ) François Marie Arouet
2 Nancy Boyd	( ) Ray Stannard Baker
3 Boz	( ) Charlotte Brontë
4 Lewis Carroll	( ) Charles Farrar Browne
5 Elia	( ) Edward Bulwer-Lytton
6 George Eliot	( ) Samuel Langhorne Clemens
7 Anatole France	( ) Louise de la Ramée
8 David Grayson	( ) Charles Dickens
9 O. Henry	( ) Charles Lutwidge Dodgson
10 Pierre Loti	( ) Mme Amantine Lucile Dudevant
11 Owen Meredith	( ) Mary Ann Evans
12 Ossian	( ) Charles Lamb
13 Ouida	( ) James MacPherson
14 Saki	( ) Edna St Vincent Millay
15 George Sand	( ) Hector Hugh Munro
16 Alice B. Toklas	( ) William Sydney Porter
17 Mark Twain	( ) Gertrude Stein
18 S. S. Van Dine	( ) Jacques Anatole Thibault
19 Voltaire	( ) Louis Marie Julien Viaud
20 Artemus Ward	( ) Willard Huntington Wright

58 · Artists in Literature. *Not all the characters in this quiz were artists, but at least they displayed an inclination toward brush or pencil. Can you identify them and name the author who created them?*

1 After his daily caning by a sadistic schoolmaster, this roly-poly scholar would cheer himself up by drawing skeletons all over his slate.

2 One of the early masterpieces of this artist was a picture of his sweetheart's foot etched on his studio wall with the point of a compass.

3 To annoy the police and his rival criminals, this modern buccaneer would leave at the scene of his crimes a small line drawing of a haloed figure.

4 Before going blind from a sword cut, he completed his masterpiece, *Melancholia*, the likeness of a woman who had known all the sorrow in the world and was laughing at it.

5 A yellowed ivy leaf painted on a brick wall outside a pneumonia patient's window by this artist was his final work.

6 The unfinished portrait of her lodger as *The Discus Thrower* remained forever unfinished when the family of her daughter's boy friend came for dinner a day ahead of time.

7 This self-centred genius died of leprosy in Tahiti, with the walls of his room covered with his greatest works.

8 So beautiful was this artist's portrait of a young man that its subject, realizing he would not always be so handsome, wished that the picture would age instead.

9 After this genius died of tuberculosis, his widow wrote a book about him and successfully sold his pictures.

10 Death caused this girl to leave her masterpiece unfinished, so that the picture of a melancholy lady on a bridge had two arms folded across her breast, two stretched out in front, and two reaching toward the moon.

59 · Brothers and Sisters. *Can you give the surnames of the brothers and sisters listed below and tell what books they are in?*

1 Tom, Sid, and Mary.
2 John, Annie, and Lizzie.
3 Michael, Digby, and John.
4 Wendy, John, and Michael.
5 Scarlett, Suellen, and Carreen.
6 Francie, Neeley, and Annie Laurie.
7 Meg, Jo, Beth, and Amy.
8 Fritz, Ernest, Jack, and Franz.
9 Marcus, Bess, Homer, and Ulysses.
10 George, Olivia, Sophia, and Moses.
11 Mabel, Elizabeth, Kate, and Isabella.
12 Ben, Polly, Joel, David, and Phronsie.
13 Jane, Elizabeth, Lydia, Kitty, and Mary.
14 Jimmy, Asia, Australia, Europena, and Billy.
15 Tom, Al, Noah, Ruthie, Winfield, and Rosasharn.
16 Renny, Meg, Eden, Piers, Finch, and Wakefield.
17 Richart, Jacob, Gerard, Giles, Sybrant, Cornelius, and Kate.
18 Elizabeth, Henrietta, Arabel, Octavius, Septimus, Alfred, Charles, Henry, and George.
19 Ann, Jolyon, James, Swithin, Roger, Julia, Hester, Nicholas, Timothy, and Susan.
20 Angela, Arnolfo, Maria, Nicolo, Beatrice, Claudia, Federigo, Pietro, Innocenza, Jacopo, and Luigi.

60 · Clocks and Watches. *Clocks or watches played an important rôle in the lives of the characters who are described below. Can you identify them and name the stories in which they appeared?*

1 At the most important moment of this character's life, his mother interrupted his father to ask if he had not forgotten to wind the clock.

2 He sold his watch, his most cherished possession, in order to buy his wife a set of combs for a Christmas present.

3 This character had a watch which was supposed to tell the day of the month, but it didn't run, even though the *best* butter was used in the works.

4 Sixteen years after he had slipped into an abandoned stone quarry and drowned, his body was identified by his gold watch and seals.

5 As a farewell gift to his favourite reporter, this hard-boiled editor presented him with his own watch, inscribed 'To the Best Newspaper Man I Know.'

6 Every timepiece in her house was stopped at twenty minutes to nine to commemorate the moment on her wedding day when her fiancé had jilted her.

7 He was the proud owner of an immense double-cased silver watch which needed only to be put back half an hour every morning and about another quarter towards the afternoon.

8 From a brief study of a watch, this detective deduced that its owner had been an eldest son, who inherited the watch from his father, was a man of untidy habits, was left with good prospects but threw away his chances, lived for some time in poverty with occasional short intervals of prosperity, finally took to drink and died.

9 Presented with a clock by his fellow workers on the occasion of his retirement from business, this elderly clerk dropped and broke it on the way home.

10 All the clocks in London were striking ten minutes to nine to inform this traveller that he was arriving late.

61 · It Could Happen to You! *Be warned by the strange experiences of the characters in this quiz and be wary of what you eat or drink. Can you name the characters and the authors who created them?*

1 This extremely fat man took an ancient Hindu recipe for loss of weight and presently found himself bumping against the ceiling.

2 Over-indulgence in some peculiar gin provided at an outdoor bowling party by a group of Dutch sailors put this man to sleep for twenty years.

3 A friar gave this girl a potion which put her into a death-like trance for forty-two hours.

4 This doctor gave four elderly friends some water from the Fountain of Youth which made them young again for an hour.

5 A potion which this doctor compounded and drank changed him into another person having all the characteristics of the evil side of his nature.

6 As long as a bite from a poisoned apple stayed in her mouth she appeared to be dead.

7 Because she once ate six pomegranate seeds, this girl had to spend six months of every year underground.

8 After they had imbibed freely of her wine, this island enchantress turned a group of sailors into swine.

9 Having been transformed by enchantment into an ass, this young man succeeded, after many trials and tribulations, in eating a rose, thereby resuming his human shape.

10 After first looking to see if there was a poison label on it, this little girl drank the contents of a bottle marked DRINK ME, and proceeded to shrink to ten inches in height.

62 · Aspects of Nature in Poetry. *This time you are asked to match up the brief nature descriptions in the column on the left with the names of the poets who originated them in the column on the right.*

1	Bee-loud glade.	( ) Matthew Arnold
2	Bleak shore.	( ) Robert Browning
3	Civil-suited morn.	( ) William Cullen Bryant
4	Cold grey stones.	( ) Robert Burns
5	Darkling plain.	( ) Lord Byron
6	Easy wind.	( ) Thomas Campbell
7	Falling dew.	( ) Samuel Taylor Coleridge
8	Gentle rain.	( ) Robert Frost
9	Glimmering landscape.	( ) Thomas Gray
10	Mossy stone.	( ) Felicia Hemans
11	Murmuring pines.	( ) John Keats
12	Murmuring stream.	( ) Henry Wadsworth Longfellow
13	Pathless woods.	( ) Edna St Vincent Millay
14	Perilous seas.	( ) John Milton
15	Quiet-coloured end of evening.	( ) William Shakespeare
16	Rock-bound coast.	( ) Percy Bysshe Shelley
17	Splendid silent sun.	( ) Alfred Tennyson
18	Untrodden snow.	( ) Walt Whitman
19	Wide wide sea.	( ) William Wordsworth
20	Wild west wind.	( ) William Butler Yeats

63 · The Sailor's Life. *From the following descriptions of the crews of famous literary ships, can you name the stories in which they appeared and the authors who created them?*

1 *The Times* and *Saturday Review* beguiled the leisure of the crew, all of whom were related by marriage to the captain.

2 So that they would be unable to hear the song of the Sirens, the ears of the crew were stopped up with wax.

3 The crew were tenderly treated by their captain, who never (or hardly ever) used bad language or abuse and always followed up his commands with an if-you-please.

4 One hundred and twenty members of the crew of a Roman battleship were rowers, who were chained to their places before a battle.

5 The crew consisted of one man, who was cook, captain, mate, bo'sun, midshipman, and crew of the captain's gig.

6 After lying dead for a week, two hundred members of the crew rose up and joined the lone survivor in sailing the ship.

7 The cook was Dutch and behaved as such, for the food that he gave the crew was a number of tons of hot-cross buns chopped up with sugar and glue.

8 All of the crew could understand the map by which their course was steered, for all 'merely conventional signs' such as islands and meridians had been omitted and it was an absolute blank.

9 The crew of a gigantic old sailing vessel, which raced through a never-ending violent storm in the south polar regions, was made up of men who appeared to be centuries old.

10 Disdaining the advice of the cabin boy (who favoured arbitration) the thirteen-man crew of a British battleship overcame a fleet of a dozen French ships.

64 · Memorable Words of Dickens Characters. *From re-reading their own words, can you identify these immortal characters from the works of Charles Dickens?*

1 'At present, and until something turns up (which I am, I may say, hourly expecting), I have nothing to bestow but advice.'

2 'Be wery careful o' vidders all your life.'

3 'Buy an annuity cheap, and make your life interesting to yourself and everyone else that watches the speculation.'

4 'Don't ask me whether I won't take none, or whether I will, but leave the bottle on the chimley-piece, and let me put my lips to it when I am so dispoged.'

5 'Father is rather vulgar, my dear. The word "papa", besides, gives a pretty form to the lips. Papa, potatoes, poultry, prunes, and prism are all very good words for the lips, especially prunes and prism.'

6 'I am a demd villain! I will fill my pockets with change for a sovereign in half-pence and drown myself in the Thames. I will become a demd, damp, moist, unpleasant body!'

7 'I am a lone, lorn creetur, and everythink goes contrairy with me.'

8 'I am well aware that I am the 'umblest person going. My mother is likewise a very 'umble person. We live in a numble abode.'

9 'I ain't quite certain where that's to be found, but, when found, make a note of.'

10 'I don't believe there ever was a man as could come out so strong under circumstances that would make other men miserable, as I could, if I could only get a chance. But I can't get a chance.'

11 'It was as true as turnips is. It was as true as taxes is. And nothing's truer than them.'

12 'I won't be prayed agin, I tell you. I can't afford it. If you must go flopping yourself down, flop in favour of your husband and child and not in opposition to 'em.'

13 'Please, sir, I want some more.'

14 'What is the odds, so long as the fire of soul is kindled at the taper of conwiviality and the wing of friendship never moults a feather?'

15 'What I want is facts. Teach these boys and girls nothing but facts. Facts alone are wanted in life. Plant nothing else, and root out everything else. Stick to facts, sir!'

65 · Chapter Headings. *The following distinctive chapter headings are taken from well-known novels. How many of them can you identify?*

1 Afternoon at Timothy's.
2 A 'Viking's Funeral.'
3 Casa da Bonnyfeather.
4 Fiddler's Hut.
5 Hot Cheeks and Tearful Eyes.
6 How to Live Well on Nothing a Year.
7 I Am Born.
8 If Love Were All!
9 Knight-Errantry as a Trade.
10 Ruined, and Going Downhill.
11 Showing Off in Sunday School.
12 Shows How First Love May Interrupt Breakfast.
13 Slaughter in the Marshes.
14 The Baker Street Irregulars.
15 The Goblin Monk.
16 The History of Cunegonde.
17 The Pursuit of a Father to Reclaim a Lost Child to Virtue.
18 The Telegraph Office.
19 The Utility of Stovepipes.
20 Under the Umbrella.
21 What I Heard in the Cracker Barrel.
22 Wool and Water.

66 · Titles Taken from Shakespeare. *Each of the twenty book titles listed below is a quotation from Shakespeare. Can you name the work from which each was borrowed?*

1 *Both Your Houses*, by MAXWELL ANDERSON.
2 *Dear Brutus*, by JAMES M. BARRIE.
3 *Tomorrow and Tomorrow*, by PHILIP BARRY.
4 *Can Such Things Be?* by AMBROSE BIERCE.
5 *This England*, by MARY ELLEN CHASE.
6 *Sad Cypress*, by AGATHA CHRISTIE.
7 *A Good Man's Love*, by ELIZABETH DE LA PASTURE.
8 *Moon Calf*, by FLOYD DELL.
9 *Ill Met by Moonlight*, by LESLIE FORD.
10 *Goodnight, Sweet Prince*, by GENE FOWLER.
11 *Under the Greenwood Tree*, by THOMAS HARDY.
12 *Twice Told Tales*, by NATHANIEL HAWTHORNE.
13 *Brave New World*, by ALDOUS HUXLEY.
14 *Told by an Idiot*, by ROSE MACAULAY.
15 *Cakes and Ale*, by SOMERSET MAUGHAM.
16 *Not So Deep as a Well*, by DOROTHY PARKER.
17 *Remembrance of Things Past*, by MARCEL PROUST.
18 *All Our Yesterdays*, by H. M. TOMLINSON.
19 *Glimpses of the Moon*, by EDITH WHARTON.
20 *Come, my Coach*, by MARJORIE WORTHINGTON.

67 · How Well-known Novels End. *Quoted below are the closing lines of ten well-known novels. Can you name both novel and author?*

1 'Rest assured, our father, rest assured. The land is not to be sold.' But over the old man's head they looked at each other and smiled.

2 There was no moon. The sky above our heads was inky black. But the sky on the horizon was not dark at all. It was shot with crimson, like a splash of blood. And the ashes blew towards us with the salt wind from the sea.

3 I had nothing now on this side of the grave to wish for: all my cares were over; my pleasure was unspeakable. It now only remained, that my gratitude in good fortune should exceed my former submission in adversity.

4 'Tomorrow, I'll think of some way to get him back. After all, tomorrow is another day.'

5 Lying on the floor was a dead man, in evening dress, with a knife in his heart. He was withered, wrinkled, and loathsome in visage. It was not till they had examined the rings that they recognized who it was.

6 'O father', said Eppie, 'what a pretty house ours is! I think nobody could be happier than we are.'

7 Come, children, let us shut up the box and the puppets, for our play is played out.

8 She glanced at the soup-plate, and, on the chance that it might after all contain something worth inspection, she awkwardly balanced on her old legs and went to it again.

9 'This new quinine stuff may prove pretty good. We'll plug along on it for two or three years, and maybe we'll get something permanent—and probably we'll fail!'

10 'For me there still remains the cocaine-bottle.' And he stretched his long white hand up for it.

68 · I Felt Such a Fool! *Characters in literature, like those in real life, occasionally suffer embarrassing moments. After reading the brief instances described below, can you identify the fictional figure and the work in which he appeared?*

1 When this gentleman asked his landlady whether she thought it a much greater expense to keep two people than to keep one, she thought he was proposing, whereas he was only thinking of employing a servant.

2 After judicious swapping of fish hooks and what not had enabled him to acquire a sufficient number of Sunday School tickets to win a Bible, this boy identified the first two apostles as David and Goliath.

3 This young clergyman made the error of thinking that the highly respectable lady milliner upon whom he was calling was a prostitute.

4 Much to the embarrassment of this social climber, her husband was unexpectedly released from jail and came home to find her entertaining a notorious member of the nobility.

5 As he started out to celebrate his twentieth wedding anniversary by dining in a neighbouring town, his horse ran away, and this luckless rider not only lost his hat, wig, and cape but also failed to arrive at his destination.

6 When this young man tried to explain to his fiancée that the woman with whom he had been intimately conversing was his mother, she didn't believe him, because the mother, who was a couple of centuries old, looked like a maid of seventeen.

7 This casual visitor caused considerable embarrassment in an English household when he mentioned that his hostess's first husband was still living.

8 To overcome his stuttering, a doctor advised this young man to speak to three complete strangers every day, but the first stranger he encountered was a pugnacious individual who addressed him first—in a stutter.

9 While he was relaxing one evening in the apartment of his doting secretary, this clergyman was surprised when the lady's husband popped in and threatened to sue him for alienation of affections.

10 At a delicate stage in this sensitive lover's advances towards an indifferent young woman her parrot began to scream blue murder.

69 · First Words of Famous Quatrains. *Printed below are the initial words of eighteen quatrains by as many different poets. All you have to do, after recognizing each stanza, is to name the author.*

1

A...............
Half............
Fair.............
Is...............

2

Ah..............
Before...........
Dust............
Sans............

3

Tiger............
In..............
What...........
Framed.........

4

Drink...........
And............
Or..............
And............

5

Far.............
Their...........
Along...........
They...........

6

Flow............
Flow............
My.............
Flow...........

7

Gather..........
Old ....
And............
Tomorrow.......

8

Guns ....
Nooses..........
Gas.............
You ....

9

Lives...........
We.............
And............
Footprints.......

10

Loveliest.........
Is...............
And............
Wearing.........

11

Maid...........
Give...........
Or.............
Keep..........

12

Music...........
Vibrates.........
Odours..........
Live............

13

Out..............
Black...........
I...............
For.............

14

Say.............
Say.............
Say.............
Jenny..........

15

Stone...........
Nor............
Minds..........
That...........

16

Strephon.........
Robin...........
But.............
And............

17

Sunset..........
And............
And.............
When..........

18

Take...........
Lift.............
Fashion'd.........
Young ....

69

70 · **Characters and Windows.** *All of the characters in this quiz had something to do with windows. From the circumstances as outlined below, can you identify them and name the authors who created them?*

1 When an invading army fired on the flag that flew from her attic window, this ninety-year-old heroine snatched it from the broken staff and waved it in defiance.

2 Threatened with a dire curse if she looked out of her window, she contented herself with seeing the world reflected in a mirror, until one day a handsome knight rode into view.

3 While she was leaning out of her tower window to let her brother-in-law caress her long blonde hair, her husband came along.

4 Cheek in hand, she leaned out of her bedroom window and soliloquized about the young man she'd met that night at a ball given by her parents.

5 To entertain a visiting stranger, this young girl used the circumstance that the French window was wide open as the foundation for a ghost story that frightened him out of the house.

6 This Transylvanian had the odd habit of emerging from a window and crawling head first down the castle wall on his nightly foraging for fresh meat.

7 While he was attempting to escape through the window of a nursery he had entered, the window was slammed shut so quickly that it cut off his shadow.

8 Returning home after eleven years of being shipwrecked and marooned on a tropical isle, he saw through the window his wife and children in a happy domestic scene with the man who had replaced him.

9 One candle in the bedroom window of her château meant, to this cavalier watching from a neighbouring farmhouse, that they would meet the next day; two, that her husband would remain at home.

10 To win a wager, this soldier sat on the outside of a sloping third-story window sill and, without holding to anything, drank off a whole bottle of rum.

71 · Antecedents of ' They '. *Each of the poetic quotations below contains the word 'they'. Do you remember in each case to what that word refers?*

1 At once they rushed together, as two eagles on one prey come rushing down together from the clouds.

2 They fought the dogs and killed the cats and bit the babies in the cradles.

3 They lie cold and low, each like a corpse within its grave.

4 They wept like anything to see such quantities of sand.

5 They stamped about and tramped about that mud till all the troupe made noises, as they ramped about, like schoolboys eating soup.

6 They groaned, they stirred, they all uprose, nor spake nor moved their eyes.

7 Through torrid tracts with fainting steps they go, where wild Altama murmurs to their woe.

8 Along the cool sequestered vale of life they kept the noiseless tenor of their way.

9 Ay, call it holy ground, the soil where first they trod; they have left unstained what there they found—freedom to worship God.

10 And they are gone! ay, ages long ago these lovers fled away into the storm.

11 They dined on mince and slices of quince which they ate with a runcible spoon.

12 They travelled by night and they slept by day, for their guide was a beautiful, wonderful star.

13 They said no word to the landlord, they drank his ale instead, but they gagged his daughter and bound her to the foot of her narrow bed.

14 And in at the windows, and in at the door, and through the walls by the thousands they pour, and down from the ceiling and up through the floor, from the right and the left, from behind and before.

15 So these were wed and merrily rang the bells, merrily rang the bells and they were wed.

16 Continuous as the stars that shine and twinkle on the milky way, they stretched in never ending line along the margin of a bay.

72 · Short-Story Openings. *Here are the opening lines of ten famous short stories. Can you name their titles and authors?*

1 'My aunt will be down presently, Mr Nuttel,' said a very self-possessed young lady of fifteen: 'in the meantime you must try and put up with me.'

2 It was a body all right.

3 True! nervous, very, very dreadfully nervous I had been and am; but why *will* you say that I am mad? The disease had sharpened my senses, not destroyed, not dulled them. Above all was the sense of hearing acute.

4 On all the roads about Goderville the peasants and their wives were coming toward the town, for it was market day. The men were walking at an easy gait, the whole body thrown forward at every movement of their long, crooked legs, mis-shapen by hard work.

5 To Sherlock Holmes, she is always *the* woman.

6 One dollar and eighty-seven cents. That was all. And sixty cents of it was in pennies.

7 It was a dark autumn night. The old banker was pacing from corner to corner of his study, recalling to his mind the party he gave in the autumn fifteen years before.

8 Marley was dead, to begin with. There is no doubt whatever about that.

9 I was very late for school that morning, and I was terribly afraid of being scolded, especially as Monsieur Hamel had told us that he should examine us on participles, and I did not know the first thing about them.

10 It was a wild and stormy night on the West Coast of Scotland. This, however, is immaterial to the present story, as the scene is not laid in the West of Scotland.

73 · **Some Famous Sisters.** *Here are some of fiction's famous sisters. Do you remember the stories in which they appeared and the authors who created them? Give yourself extra credit if you can also name the sisters.*

1 These five unmarried daughters of an underpaid rector played cards to determine which of them should marry their father's new assistant.

2 After ten years of separation a New Zealand pioneer wrote a lengthy letter proposing that the girl he loved come out and marry him—and absent-mindedly addressed it to her sister, who accepted.

3 These sweet old ladies took friendless and lonely old men into their Brooklyn home, poisoned them, and interred the bodies in the basement with appropriate burial services.

4 Romance came on the same night to both of these quarrelsome, frustrated sisters, who lived in a run-down district of London with their half-paralysed father.

5 Daughters of a linen-draper, they were separated when one eloped to Paris with a travelling salesman, but were reunited more than twenty years later.

6 One of the ten daughters of a poor curate, she married an impecunious young barrister and took most of her sisters to live with them in their three-room suite.

7 When a wealthy young bachelor moved into their neighbourhood it was naturally of great interest to these five marriageable sisters and their mother.

8 These four sisters celebrated Christmas by presenting for their friends *The Witch's Curse*, a melodramatic tragedy which one of them had written.

9 Because this girl refused to express her love for her father in extravagant flattery, he disowned her and divided his estate between her two older sisters.

10 While this girl was being proposed to by a pirate, her many many sisters sympathetically shut their eyes and talked about the weather.

74 · Sub-Titles of Well-known Books. *Listed below are the not-so-well-known sub-titles of twenty well-known books and plays. How many of them do you recognize?*

1 ...., or *Life Among the Lowly.*
2 ...., *A Novel Without A Hero.*
3 ...., or *The Slave of Duty.*
4 ...., *A Romance of Exmoor.*
5 ...., or *The Weaver of Raveloe.*
6 ...., or *Virtue Rewarded.*
7 ...., *A Tale of the Christ.*
8 ...., *A Romance of the Tropical Forest.*
9 ...., or *What You Will.*
10 ...., *A Comedy of Justice.*
11 ...., or *Comforting Thoughts about the Bison.*
12 ...., *A Novel of Husbands and Wives.*
13 ...., or *The Mistakes of a Night.*
14 ...., or *The Skeleton in the Cupboard.*
15 ...., *A Tale of Flodden Field.*
16 ...., *A Tale of Arcadie.*
17 ...., or *Prison Life in Siberia.*
18 ...., *A Comedy of Morals.*
19 ...., or *What Would Jesus Do?*
20 ...., or *The Modern Prometheus.*

74

75 · Characters Concerned with Flowers. *The characters in this quiz were memorably associated with flowers. From the brief descriptions given below, can you identify each one and name the author who created him?*

1 Because of his morbid love of admiration, this poet would walk down Piccadilly with a poppy or a lily in his hand.

2 She sold flowers in Covent Garden until taken in hand by a phonetics expert.

3 She had a garden of roses and lilies fair on a lawn.

4 Fantastically dressed in straws and flowers, she scattered rosemary for remembrance and pansies for thoughts.

5 Every year this dashing Englishman received a single red rose from the Queen of Ruritania.

6 Everywhere she went—and she went everywhere—she carried a bouquet of camellias.

7 The hobby of this celebrated detective is the cultivation of orchids every afternoon from four to six.

8 With some water from the Fountain of Youth this doctor revived a rose given to him by his sweetheart fifty-five years previously.

9 This little girl found herself in a flower garden containing a tigerlily, a rose, a violet, a larkspur, and several daisies, all of which could talk.

10 This collector acquired a repulsive-looking orchid which first absorbed and then put out as blossoms the heads of several houseflies, followed by the family cat, Cousin Jane, and finally the collector himself.

76 · 'It's the Syme the Whole World Over.' *'Love 'em and leave 'em' was the motto of the villains responsible for this quiz. From the brief descriptions of their ungentlemanly behaviour as sketched below, can you name each of these low characters and the story in which he appears?*

1 On the eve of her marriage to her cousin, an uncouth fisherman with a heart of gold, this wealthy playboy persuaded a trusting maiden to elope with him to France, where, not long after, he left her with the suggestion that she marry his valet.

2 Persuaded by this unprincipled scoundrel that her husband's frequent business conferences with a pretty neighbour were not at all innocent, she eloped with him and found herself deserted a year later with a nameless unborn child.

3 This worldly travelling salesman persuaded a highly respectable draper's daughter to elope with him, married her reluctantly, and eventually left her, penniless and ill, in Paris.

4 When this fortune hunter discovered, a few months after he had married her, that his bride had no wealth beyond what he had already squandered, he left her at a wayside inn, hurried home, and skipped out with all the household furnishings, including her clothes.

5 This perfidious villain kidnapped a not-too-unwilling clergyman's daughter and went through what he thought was a fake wedding ceremony, only to find out later that the licence and the priest were both genuine.

6 To destroy his step-daughter's faith in men and thus secure her fortune for himself, this cold-blooded scoundrel disguised himself, wooed and won the girl, and then left her waiting at the church.

7 This American naval officer married a Japanese geisha and then sailed away after promising to return when the robins were nesting.

8 After this light-minded cad had trifled with the affections of a pretty dairymaid, he went off to join his regiment, leaving his victim to be convicted of the murder of their child.

9 He was the foreman in a shirt factory and she was a working girl, and after a while, in order to improve his social standing, he accidentally drowned her on purpose.

10 At a high society ball which they attended on their honeymoon, this British officer left his bride sitting in a corner while he tried to persuade another man's wife to elope with him.

77 · Last Lines of Sonnets. *This quiz is for those poetry lovers who read sonnets all the way through to the last line. They are invited to match up the twenty last lines listed below with the names of the poets who wrote them.*

1 All losses are restored and sorrows end. ( ) Arnold
2 And all that mighty heart is lying still! ( ) Blunt
3 And Death shall be no more: Death, thou ( ) Brooke
  shalt die!
4 And Heaven and Hell may meet—yet never ( ) Browning
  we.
5 And must I lose a soul's inheritance? ( ) Byron
6 And round their narrow lips the mould falls ( ) Donne
  close.
7 And then you suddenly cried, and turned away.( ) Drayton
8 And weep the more, because I weep in vain. ( ) Gray
9 Even if we cease life is a miracle. ( ) Keats
10 Find their sole voice in that victorious brow. ( ) Longfellow
11 'Fool!' said my Muse to me, 'look in thy ( ) Masefield
  heart and write.'
12 For none can call againe the passèd time. ( ) Milton
13 For they appeal from tyranny to God. ( ) C. Rossetti
14 From death to life thou might'st him yet ( ) D. Rossetti
  recover.
15 Silent, upon a peak in Darien. ( ) Shakespeare
16 Than that you should remember and be sad. ( ) Shelley
17 They also serve who only stand and wait. ( ) Sidney
18 The lone and level sands stretch far away. ( ) Spenser
19 Thou may'st love on through love's eternity. ( ) Wilde
20 While the eternal ages watch and wait. ( ) Wordsworth

78 · **Twice-married Women.** *Each of the women in this quiz was married twice. From the brief descriptions given below, can you identify them and name the author who created them?*

1 When her first husband, a British banker, died while they were travelling down the Mississippi, she married his prosperous Louisiana business associate whom she had known as a child in Italy.

2 After her first husband was discovered to be a bigamist, she married the rising young printer with whom she had always been in love.

3 After divorcing her first husband, an irresponsible poet, she married his half-brother, a horse breeder.

4 When her first husband died, leaving her to bear a posthumous child, she married a tall, dark, and handsome villain who browbeat her to death.

5 Many years after she had spurned a stolid and dependable farmer to marry a dashing but worthless soldier she found happiness with her first suitor.

6 After being long separated from and finally divorced by a man of property, she married his cousin.

7 Her second husband was considerably upset when a casual caller hinted that her first husband, who was supposed to have died in Australia, was still alive.

8 Eleven years after the disappearance of her sailor-husband, she presumed that he was dead and married a man who had been the childhood friend of both of them.

9 Her first husband was killed in the battle of Waterloo, and it was many many years later before she recovered from her grief and married the man who had always truly loved her but never declared himself.

10 After her first husband had been most foully murdered by his brother, she married the brother.

79 · Characters who were Disguised. *For one reason or another, many literary characters have at times assumed disguises. Can you identify the nine briefly described below and name the stories in which they appeared?*

1 Disguised as a learned doctor of laws, this bride went into court and saved the life of her husband's best friend.

2 Fleeing from his father's court to escape marriage with an elderly lady, this prince assumed the disguise of a Second Trombone and became the hat passer of a small band.

3 Dressed in a calico gown and a sunbonnet, this runaway boy called on a woman who was a newcomer in his home town to get the latest news about his disappearance.

4 Disguised as an elderly, deformed bibliophile, this celebrated detective returned to London three years after his reported death in Switzerland.

5 Curious to find out what men were really like, this young girl disguised herself as a cavalier, travelled about France, and encountered some amazing adventures.

6 Because he thought his wife was in the mood to take a lover, this actor disguised himself as a Russian guardsman and wooed her.

7 When the sudden need for a chaperon occurred, this young man, a member of the Oxford University Dramatic Society, disguised himself as his friend's aunt from Brazil, where the nuts come from.

8 Banished from his court by her uncle, the duke, she disguised herself as a shepherd and fled to the Forest of Arden.

9 Though this sultan was the political enemy of Richard the Lion-Heart, he disguised himself as an Arabian physician, entered Richard's camp, and cured the king of an Asiatic fever.

80 · In the Middle of the Night. *Unusual things happen in the middle of the night, as the ten instances from literature's pages that make up this quiz will show. Can you name the characters concerned and the authors who created them?*

1 Awakened by a demoniac laugh, this governess opened her bedroom door, discovered that smoke was pouring from her employer's room, dashed in and threw a basin of water on his blazing bed.

2 In the middle of a chilly April night this young lady left her father's castle, went out in the woods to pray for her absent lover, and encountered a beautiful, desolate and highly sinister lady.

3 You can imagine this girl's surprise when she woke up and saw the man she loved in the adjoining sitting-room in the act of stealing a valuable gem.

4 Night after night while his other schoolmates slept, this little boy sat in the dark and told stories from the classics to the school hero.

5 With cat-like tread, under the leadership of this 21-year-old hero, a band of pirates stole upon their prey, a major-general and his bevy of beautiful daughters.

6 While his beloved lay asleep in her bedroom, he emerged from a closet with a variety of tasty foods and set out a picnic lunch, then softly serenaded her until she woke up.

7 This impulsive young lady crouched on the window ledge of her bedroom, clutching her knees tightly against her chest, and longed to fly away into the soft spring night.

8 In the middle of the night she would rise from her bed and, still asleep, go through the motions of washing her hands.

9 In the middle of the night he emerged from a window in his castle, crawled face down the castle wall, and returned much later with a half-smothered baby in a handbag.

10 With a companion, this boy lay hidden in the village cemetery and watched the local doctor, with the help of a couple of disreputable characters, resurrect a recently buried corpse.

81 · Fathers and Sons. *This quiz is concerned with some of fiction's famous fathers and sons. Can you name the character called for, as well as the author who created him?*

1 Fighting incognito on a battlefield this warrior mortally wounded his opponent and then found that the latter was his own son.

2 In the post-war depression this ex-army captain took a menial job as a hotel porter in order to provide a decent living for his young son.

3 This pompous banker was pleased when his dying wife gave birth to a son, for he planned to take him into the business, but his plans were upset when the boy died while still a child.

4 This son was the victim of his father's 'system' of education which excluded all interests normal to a growing boy.

5 A tyrant commanded this father to demonstrate his skill with the crossbow by shooting an apple off his son's head at 100 yards.

6 His father's ghost appeared to this son and urged him to avenge his most foul and unnatural murder.

7 Fulfilling the prophecy of an oracle, this son unwittingly killed his father and married his own mother.

8 This father's anxiety that his son had a well-built nose and a good name was ruined when the child's nose was squashed by the doctor's forceps and he was mistakenly christened with the name that the father most despised.

9 When this son, against his father's wishes, married the newly-impoverished girl to whom he had been betrothed since childhood, the father deleted his name from the family Bible.

10 Because his father was the town drunkard, this boy never had to go to school or church and was the envy of every other boy in St Petersburg, Missouri.

82 · **How to Begin a Novel.** *This quiz may not teach you how to write a novel, but it will show you how ten well-known novels begin. After reading these opening lines, can you name each novel and its author?*

1 I was ever of the opinion that the honest man who married and brought up a large family did more service than he who continued single and only talked of population.

2 As I walked through the wilderness of this world, I lighted on a certain place where there was a Den, and I laid me down in that place to sleep.

3 I wish either my father or my mother, or indeed both of them, as they were in duty both equally bound to it, had minded what they were about when they begot me.

4 It was the best of times, it was the worst of times, it was the age of wisdom, it was the age of foolishness, it was the epoch of belief, it was the epoch of incredulity. . . .

5 It is a truth universally acknowledged, that a single man in possession of a good fortune must be in want of a wife.

6 Call me Ishmael. Some years ago—never mind how long precisely—having little or no money in my purse, and nothing particular to interest me on shore, I thought I would sail about a little and see the watery part of the world.

7 He was born with the gift of laughter and a sense that the world was mad.

8 When you are getting on in years (but not ill, of course), you get very sleepy at times, and the hours seem to pass like lazy cattle moving across a landscape.

9 Between the villages of Aubière and Romagnat in the ancient Province of Auvergne there is an old road that comes suddenly over the top of a high hill.

10 The towers of Zenith aspired above the morning mist; austere towers of steel and cement and limestone, sturdy as cliffs and delicate as silver rods. They were neither citadels nor churches, but frankly and beautifully office-buildings.

83 · Requests of Poets. *Poets are always asking for something, as this quiz demonstrates. From their requests, as quoted below, can you identify the poets?*

1 Tell me the tales that to me were so dear, long, long ago.

2 If I should die, think only this of me: that there's some corner of a foreign field that is forever England.

3 Grow old along with me! The best is yet to be.

4 Gie me a cannie hour at e'en, my arms about my dearie, O!

5 Give, oh give me back my heart!

6 Tell me where all past years are, or who cleft the devil's foot.

7 Let me live in a house by the side of the road and be a friend to man.

8 Make me a child again just for tonight.

9 Drink to me only with thine eyes.

10 Come live with me and be my love.

11 All I ask is a merry yarn from a laughing fellow-rover.

12 So fold thyself, my dearest, thou, and slip into my bosom and be lost in me.

13 When I am dead, my dearest, sing no sad songs for me.

14 But come thou goddess fair and free.

15 Take, O take those lips away, that so sweetly were forsworn.

16 Make me thy Lyre.

17 Under the wide and starry sky dig the grave and let me lie.

18 Come to me in the silence of the night; come in the speaking silence of a dream.

19 Give me but what this riband bound, take all the rest the sun goes round!

20 Give me the splendid silent sun, with all his beams full-dazzling!

84 · Gifts in Literature. *Gifts given or received by literary characters are described in this quiz. Can you name the characters concerned as well as the stories in which they appear?*

1 After this man had stolen six silver plates from a benevolent bishop and had been captured and brought back, the bishop declared that they had been a gift and added to them a pair of silver candlesticks.

2 Upon their engagement she gave him a ring which he swore he would die before parting with, but he gave it away to the first person who asked for it.

3 She sold her beautiful long hair to buy her husband a watch fob, while he sold his watch to buy her a set of combs.

4 During his convalescence this invalid received ten thousand cockroaches, an octopus, four penguins, and an Egyptian mummy case.

5 Travelling with the Three Wise Men, he carried a sapphire, a ruby, and a pearl, which he intended as gifts for the Christ-child, but he parted from his fellow philosophers and gave the jewels to the needy instead.

6 The gift of a vacuum cleaner, even though there was no electricity to run it, elevated this woman to the peak of the social scale in her community.

7 In an effort to patch up a quarrel with his new girl friend, this boy proffered his most prized possession, a brass knob from the top of an andiron.

8 When this child was born, his neighbours gave him a silver tobacco box, a navy revolver, a diamond breast pin, a diamond ring, a slung shot, a Bible, a golden spur, a silver teaspoon, and a pair of surgeon's shears.

9 For Christmas this little girl received from her aunt a tiny match box containing ten pennies, each one covered with gilt paint.

10 Presented with the traditional copy of Johnson's Dictionary upon her departure from an academy for young ladies, this sweet girl graduate tossed it out of the carriage window as she was driven away.

85 · Characters who were very Sick. *The characters in this quiz had highly memorable illnesses. Can you identify them and name the author who created them?*

1 On a slaving ship a thousand miles from land this priest struggled deliriously through a siege of yellow fever.

2 So ill of swamp fever that he was unable to talk, this persistent optimist feebly wrote 'jolly!' on a slate.

3 Murmuring the name of the only man she had ever loved, this lonely courtesan died, after a long and painful illness, of tuberculosis.

4 Dying of gangrenous infection in his leg on an African hunting trip, this author thought about his past.

5 After four days of steady drinking, this alcoholic imagined that he saw a mouse come out of a hole in the wall and a bat attack it.

6 Parted from her betrothed in her youth, she searched for him all over the nation and finally found him, an old man, dying of the plague in a Philadelphia almshouse.

7 In a hut in Tahiti, on the walls of which he had painted his masterpiece, this artist died of leprosy.

8 A victim of catalepsy, she was buried alive in the family vault by her twin brother.

9 After nursing her lover through the great plague of London, this beauty fell ill of the same disease.

10 The breath-taking beauty of this actress's face looked horribly altered when she died of smallpox in a Paris hotel.

86 · Repeated Words and Phrases. *The repeated words and phrases in this quiz were taken from familiar poems. Can you identify the poem or name the poet?*

1 All, all are sleeping, sleeping, sleeping on the hill.
2 Alone, alone, all, all alone!
3 Bells, bells, bells, bells, bells, bells, bells!
4 Boomlay, boomlay, boomlay, boom! Boomlay, boomlay, boomlay, boom!
5 Boots—boots—boots—boots!
6 Break, break, break!
7 Come hither, come hither!
8 Come hither, come hither, come hither.
9 Dying, dying, dying.
10 Get up, get up!
11 Half a league, half a league, half a league!
12 Happy, happy, happy!
13 Heart! heart! heart!
14 He knows—He knows!
15 In lilac-time, in lilac-time, in lilac-time.
16 Look away! look away! look away!
17 Never, never, never, never, never!
18 More happy love! more happy, happy love!
19 O hush, O hush! thy tears my words are steeping. O hush, hush, hush . . .
20 Stitch—stitch—stitch!

87 · Who is ' He ' ? *In these quotations from well-known poems, can you identify the 'he' in each and his creator?*

1 A cannon ball took off his legs, so he laid down his arms.
2 A sadder and a wiser man he rose the morrow morn.
3 Full well they laughed with counterfeited glee
  At all his jokes, for many a joke had he.
4 He came to ask what he had found
  That was so large and smooth and round.
5 He felt the cheering power of spring,
  It made him whistle, it made him sing.
6 He has outsoared the shadow of our night.
7 He sets his Jenny on his knee,
  All in his Highland dress;
  For brawlie weel he ken'd the way
  To please a bonie lass.
8 He smiled as he sat by the table
  With a smile that was childlike and bland.
9 He stayed not for brake, and he stopp'd not for stone,
  He swam the Eske river, where ford there was none.
10 He was a gentleman from soul to crown,
  Clean favoured, and imperially slim.
11 His brow is wet with honest sweat, he earns whate'er he can.
12 In enterprise of martial kind, when there was any fighting,
  He led his regiment from behind (He found it less exciting).
13 Into her dream he melted, as the rose
  Blendeth its odour with the violet.
14 The waters wild went o'er his child, and he was left lamenting.
15 With nectar pure his oozy locks he laves
  And hears the unexpressive nuptial song.
16 With sobs and tears he sorted out those of the largest size,
  Holding his pocket-handkerchief before his streaming eyes.

88 · Scrambled Names of Dickens Characters. *Listed below are the names of forty-eight prominent Dickens characters which have been fiendishly scrambled almost beyond recognition. If, within an hour, you can unscramble half of them you've done well; thirty-five of them marks you excellent; all of them, you're a genius.*

1 ALARC GETTYGOP
2 AMHOST STRADDLE
3 ARIHU PEHE
4 BYTSEE WORTODOT
5 CHARRID VISWELLER
6 CROWDKAF QUESSER
7 CULIE EMATENT
8 CYTAR NAPMUT
9 DENYYS NACTOR
10 DRAWED STOREMUND
11 DREFAL GENJIL
12 DROLAH PLIKOSEM
13 GUSUTUSA SADGORNSS
14 HANO YOPLLACE
15 HONJ SPREJA
16 HURRAT MACLENN
17 INTRAM UZWETZILCH
18 KRAM PLEATY
19 KWISLIN CRABWEIM
20 LARNICOE BRIMBLE
21 LASSI GEWG
22 LEBA CHAWMTIG
23 LILIMAW TRIROD
24 LUPA MODEBY

25 LYLDO VENDAR
26 MANSOPS BARSS
27 MOASHT DDGGRRAIN
28 MONIS PITTERPAT
29 MUSEAL KIKICCPW
30 MUSICDONE FINFOB
31 NAILED PULIQ
32 NUASS PRIPEN
33 RACHELS YADRAN
34 RYJER HENCRURC
35 SEEBYT GRIP
36 SEERTH MOSSMUNER
37 SEJAM FETHERSORT
38 SHEERET GEEFRAD
39 SHELCAR CYREEBLEH
40 SLACHION BLINCKEY
41 TENTIAN SMURCLEM
42 THINLEANA NIKLEW
43 THUR PHINC
44 THYRIAC SPIFFNECK
45 VOILER STWIT
46 WINED DODOR
47 YABNARB GRUDE
48 ZENEBERE COGORES

Answers

Answers

1 · First Lines of Famous Poems.

1 *My Garden*, by T. E. BROWN
2 *Endymion*, by KEATS
3 *Locksley Hall*, by TENNYSON
4 *To Celia*, by JONSON
5 *To the Virgins to Make Much of Time*, by HERRICK
6 *Go and Catch a Falling Star*, by DONNE
7 *Rabbi Ben Ezra*, by ROBERT BROWNING
8 *To a Skylark*, by SHELLEY
9 *L'Allegro*, by MILTON
10 *It is a Beauteous Evening, Calm and Free*, by WORDSWORTH
11 *A Leave Taking*, by SWINBURNE
12 *The Prisoner of Chillon*, by BYRON
13 *The Blessed Damozel*, by D. G. ROSSETTI
14 *Elegy Written in a Country Churchyard*, by GRAY
15 *Dover Beach*, by MATTHEW ARNOLD
16 *Ulalume*, by POE
17 *The Lady of the Lake*, by SCOTT
18 *Christabel*, by COLERIDGE
19 *The Harlot's House*, by WILDE
20 *With Rue My Heart is Laden*, by A. E. HOUSMAN

2 · What the Well-dressed Character Wears

1 Miss Havisham, in *Great Expectations*, by DICKENS
2 Scarlett O'Hara, in *Gone with the Wind, by* MARGARET MITCHELL
3 *The Highwayman*, by ALFRED NOYES
4 Malvolio, in *Twelfth Night*, by SHAKESPEARE
5 *Gertrude the Governess*, by STEPHEN LEACOCK
6 *Gunga Din*, by KIPLING
7 Hester Prynne, in *The Scarlet Letter*, by NATHANIEL HAWTHORNE
8 *Little Black Sambo*, by HELEN BANNERMAN
9 *The Pied Piper of Hamelin*, by ROBERT BROWNING
10 Humpty-Dumpty, in *Through the Looking Glass, by* LEWIS CARROLL

3 · Famous Words of Famous People

1 Polonius, in *Hamlet*, by SHAKESPEARE
2 Sydney Carton, in *A Tale of Two Cities*, by DICKENS
3 Paul Revere, in *Paul Revere's Ride*, by LONGFELLOW
4 *Horatius*, by THOMAS MACAULAY
5 Juliet, in *Romeo and Juliet*, by SHAKESPEARE
6 Sherlock Holmes, in *The Adventure of the Norwood Builder*, by CONAN DOYLE
7 Humpty-Dumpty, in *Through the Looking Glass*, by LEWIS CARROLL
8 Pooh-Bah, in *The Mikado*, by W. S. GILBERT
9 Jacques, in *As You Like It*, by SHAKESPEARE
10 Wilkins Micawber, in *David Copperfield*, by DICKENS
11 *Rip Van Winkle*, as played by JOSEPH JEFFERSON
12 James Fitz-James, in *The Lady of the Lake*, by SCOTT
13 Uncle Tom, in *Uncle Tom's Cabin*, by STOWE
14 *The Highwayman*, by ALFRED NOYES
15 *Abou Ben Adhem*, by LEIGH HUNT

16 Pippa, in *Pippa Passes*, by ROBERT BROWNING

17 Dr Primrose, in *The Vicar of Wakefield*, by OLIVER GOLDSMITH

18 Sir Joseph Porter, in *H.M.S. Pinafore*, by W. S. GILBERT

4 · Gentlemen of the Cloth

1 Dr Primrose, in *The Vicar of Wakefield*, by OLIVER GOLDSMITH

2 Reverend Arthur Dimmesdale, in *The Scarlet Letter*, by NATHANIEL HAWTHORNE

3 Friar Laurence, in *Romeo and Juliet*, by SHAKESPEARE

4 Rustico, in *The Decameron*, by BOCCACCIO

5 *Tartuffe*, by MOLIÈRE

6 Mr Collins, in *Pride and Prejudice*, by JANE AUSTEN

7 Saint Maël, in *Penguin Island*, by ANATOLE FRANCE

8 Bishop Hatto, in *God's Judgment on a Wicked Bishop*, by ROBERT SOUTHEY

9 Father Paul, in *Gentle Alice Brown*, by W. S. GILBERT

10 Alfred Davidson, in *Rain*, by SOMERSET MAUGHAM

5 · Gilbert and Sullivan

1 Captain Corcoran, in *Pinafore*

2 Major General Stanley, in *The Pirates of Penzance*

3 Katisha, in *The Mikado*

4 The Lord Chancellor, in *Iolanthe*

5 Sir Joseph Porter, in *Pinafore*

6 Frederic, in *The Pirates of Penzance*

7 Nanki-Poo, in *The Mikado*

8 Sir Ruthven Murgatroyd, in *Ruddigore*

9 The Judge, in *Trial by Jury*

10 Little Buttercup, in *Pinafore*

11 Ruth, in *The Pirates of Penzance*

12 Pooh-Bah, in *The Mikado*

13 The Duke of Plaza Toro, in *The Gondoliers*

14 Reginald Bunthorne, in *Patience*

15 King Gama, in *Princess Ida*

16 Yum-Yum, in *The Mikado*

6 · Favourite Foods of Famous People

1 Cherry pie and currant wine

2 Imaginary

3 Beer

4 Several dozen cream tarts

5 Gooseberry wine

6 Toasted cheese

7 169 Pancakes

8 Expanded like a telescope

9 Cucumber sandwiches

10 Luke-warm water

7 · Twenty Questions

1 *The Vision of Sir Launfal*, by JAMES RUSSELL LOWELL

2 *Ode to the West Wind*, by SHELLEY

3 *The Man with the Hoe*, by EDWIN MARKHAM

4 *A Child's Garden of Verses*, by ROBERT LOUIS STEVENSON

5 *Sonnet XVIII*, by SHAKESPEARE

6 *The Tiger*, by BLAKE

7 *To the Cuckoo*, by WORDSWORTH

8 *Divine Songs*, by ISAAC WATTS

9 *Song from Aglaura*, by SUCKLING

10 *Ode to a Nightingale*, by KEATS

11 *The Deacon's Masterpiece*, by OLIVER WENDELL HOLMES

12 *Elegy Written in a Country Churchyard*, by GRAY

13 *Christabel*, by SAMUEL TAYLOR COLERIDGE

14 *Ode to Tobacco*, by CHARLES S. CALVERLY

15 *Sonnet on His Blindness*, by MILTON

16 *Ballad of Dead Ladies*, by FRANÇOIS VILLON

17 *The Cataract of Lodore*, by SOUTHEY

18 *A Kiss*, by AUSTIN DOBSON

19 *A Song for St Cecilia's Day*, by DRYDEN

20 *Leisure*, by W. H. DAVIES

8 · Fiction's Famous Servants

1 *Gunga Din*, by KIPLING

2 Jeeves, in *Jeeves* and many other stories by P. G. WODEHOUSE

3 Mrs Bardell, in *Pickwick Papers*, by DICKENS

4 Morgiana, in *Ali Baba and the Forty Thieves*, from *The Arabian Nights*, translated by RICHARD BURTON

5 Gabriel Betteredge, in *The Moonstone*, by WILKIE COLLINS

6 Pomona, in *Rudder Grange*, by FRANK STOCKTON

7 Ruggles, in *Ruggles of Red Gap*, by HARRY LEON WILSON

8 Ruth, in *The Pirates of Penzance*, by W. S. GILBERT

9 Mrs Hudson, in the Sherlock Holmes stories, by CONAN DOYLE

10 Pamela Andrews, in *Pamela*, by SAMUEL RICHARDSON

9 · Card Players in Literature

1 Richard Swiveller, in *The Old Curiosity Shop*, by DICKENS

2 Phileas Fogg, in *Around the World in Eighty Days*, by JULES VERNE

3 Belinda, in *The Rape of the Lock*, by ALEXANDER POPE

4 Ah Sin, in *Plain Language from Truthful James*, by BRET HARTE

5 Sarah Battle, in *Mrs Battle's Opinions on Whist*, by CHARLES LAMB

6 Dangerous Dan McGrew, in *The Shooting of Dan McGrew*, by ROBERT W. SERVICE

7 Prince Florizel, in *The Suicide Club*, by ROBERT LOUIS STEVENSON

8 Philo Vance, in *The Canary Murder Case*, by S. S. VAN DINE

9 Gaylord Ravenal, in *Show Boat*, by EDNA FERBER

10 John Oakhurst, in *The Outcasts of Poker Flat*, by BRET HARTE

10 · Characters who Wept

1 *The Blessed Damozel*, by D. G. ROSSETTI

2 *Alice Fell*, by WORDSWORTH

3 *Isabella*, by KEATS

4 The Walrus, in *Through the Looking Glass*, by LEWIS CARROLL

5 Wakefield Whiteoak, in *Jalna*, by by MAZO DE LA ROCHE

6 *Oenone*, by TENNYSON

7 Ruksh, in *Sohrab and Rustum*, by MATTHEW ARNOLD

8 Ruth, in *Ode to a Nightingale*, by KEATS

9 Alice, in *Ben Bolt*, by THOMAS DUNN ENGLISH

10 Mariana, in *Measure for Measure*, by SHAKESPEARE

11 · Three-word Quotations

1 *My Last Duchess*, by ROBERT BROWNING

2 *The Raven*, by POE

3 *To Celia*, by JONSON

4 *Go, Lovely Rose*, by WALLER

5 *Goodbye*, by EMERSON

6 *The Ancient Mariner*, by COLERIDGE

7 *Sonnet CXVI*, by SHAKESPEARE

8 *Dover Beach*, by MATTHEW ARNOLD

9 *Essay on Man*, by POPE

10 *A Psalm of Life*, by LONGFELLOW

11 *Elegy Written in a Country Churchyard*, by GRAY

12 *La Belle Dame Sans Merci*, by KEATS

13 *Ozymandias*, by SHELLEY

14 *Résumé*, by PARKER

15 *The Deserted Village*, by GOLDSMITH

16 *Woodman, Spare that Tree !* by MORRIS

17 *In Flanders Field*, by MCCRAE

18 *On His Blindness*, by MILTON

19 *The Soldier*, by BROOKE

20 *We are Seven*, by WORDSWORTH

12 · Characters who were Drowned

1 Andy Hawks, in *Showboat*, by EDNA FERBER

2 Ham Peggotty, in *David Copperfield*, by DICKENS

3 Dr Wayne Hudson, in *The Magnificent Obsession*, by LLOYD DOUGLAS

4 Virginia de la Tour, in *Paul and Virginia*, by BERNARDIN DE SAINT-PIERRE

5 Stephen Dowling Botts, in *Huckleberry Finn*, by MARK TWAIN

6 *Lucy Gray*, by WORDSWORTH

7 Ophelia, in *Hamlet*, by SHAKESPEARE

8 *Clementine*, by PERCY MONTROSS

9 Maggie Tulliver, in *The Mill on the Floss*, by GEORGE ELIOT

10 Captain Ahab, in *Moby Dick*, by HERMAN MELVILLE

13 · Characters and Hats

1 *Penrod*, by BOOTH TARKINGTON

2 Rhett Butler, in *Gone with the Wind*, by MARGARET MITCHELL

3 The Caller, in *The Lost Silk Hat*, by LORD DUNSANY

4 Iris March, in *The Green Hat*, by MICHAEL ARLEN

5 Sherlock Holmes, in *The Adventure of the Blue Carbuncle*, by CONAN DOYLE

6 Father Brown, in many stories by G. K. CHESTERTON

7 Yancey Cravat, in *Cimarron*, by EDNA FERBER

8 Gessler, in *William Tell*, by SCHILLER

9 Martin Vanderhof, in *You Can't Take It with You*, by GEORGE KAUFMAN and MOSS HART

10 The Mad Hatter, in *Alice in Wonderland*, by LEWIS CARROLL

14 · Dickens Characters

1 (a) Oliver Twist, (b) Nicholas Nickleby and Smike, (c) David Copperfield, (d) John Harmon
2 (a) Wackford Squeers, (b) Dr Strong, (c) Dr Blimber, (d) Miss Twinkleton, in *Edwin Drood*
3 (a) Mrs Jarley, (b) Gabriel Varden, (c) Mr Sleary in *Hard Times*, (d) Mme Mantalini, in *Nicholas Nickleby*
4 (a) Dick Swiveller, in *Old Curiosity Shop*, Mr Mell, in *David Copperfield*, and Jack Redburn, in *Master Humphrey's Clock* all played the flute—badly, (b) Tom Pinch, in *Martin Chuzzlewit* and John Jasper, in *Edwin Drood*, (c) Frederick Dorrit, in *Little Dorrit* played the clarionet (Dickens' spelling), (d) Prince Turveydrop, in *Bleak House* played the kit, a tiny three-stringed violin used by dancing masters
5 (a) Tiny Tim, (b) Captain Cuttle, (c) Silas Wegg, in *Our Mutual Friend*, (d) Sim Tappertit, in *Barnaby Rudge* lost the legs of which he was so proud during the Gordon riots
6 (a) Sydney Carton, (b) Krook, the filthy junk dealer, in *Bleak House*, (c) Stephen Blackpool, in *Hard Times*, (d) the pantomime actor in Jem Hutley's tale in *Pickwick Papers*
7 (a) Nancy was murdered by Bill Sykes, in *Oliver Twist*, (b) Mr Tulkington, in *Bleak House*, (c) Tigg Montague was murdered by Jonas Chuzzlewit, (d) the elder Mr Haredale was murdered by Barnaby Rudge, Sr
8 (a) Arabella Allen married Mr Winkle, in *Pickwick Papers*, (b) Esther Summerson married Allan Woodcourt, in *Bleak House*, (c) Dora Spenlow and Agnes Wickfield, (d) Lizzie Hexam married Eugene Wrayburn, in *Our Mutual Friend*
9 (a) Oliver Twist, (b) Amy Dorrit, (c) Paul Dombey, (d) David Copperfield
10 (a) The Peggottys, Mrs Gummidge, and Little Em'ly, (b) Sir Leicester Dedlock, Lady Dedlock, and Mrs Rouncewell in *Bleak House*, (c) John Willet and his son Joe, in *Barnaby Rudge*, (d) Mr Pickwick

15 · Second lines of Famous Poems

1 *Sea Fever*, by MASEFIELD
2 *The Ancient Mariner*, by COLERIDGE
3 *The Destruction of Sennacherib*, by BYRON
4 *To a Skylark*, by SHELLEY
5 *Horatius*, by MACAULAY
6 *Requiem*, by STEVENSON
7 *How They Brought the Good News from Ghent to Aix*, by ROBERT BROWNING
8 *Sonnet XXX*, by SHAKESPEARE
9 *Break, Break, Break*, by TENNYSON
10 *The Battle of Blenheim*, by SOUTHEY
11 *To the Virgins to Make Much of Time*, by HERRICK
12 *The Cow*, by NASH
13 *Why so Pale and Wan?* by SUCKLING
14 *Go, Lovely Rose*, by WALLER
15 *The Shooting of Dan McGrew*, by SERVICE
16 *Ulalume*, by POE
17 *Elegy Written in a Country Churchyard*, by GRAY
18 *The Highwayman*, by NOYES
19 *The Eve of St Agnes*, by KEATS
20 *O Captain, My Captain*, by WHITMAN

16 · As the Curtain Falls

1 *Hamlet*, by SHAKESPEARE

2 *A Doll's House*, by HENRIK IBSEN

3 *The Cherry Orchard*, by ANTON CHEKHOV

4 *The Twelve Pound Look*, by JAMES M. BARRIE

5 *The Second Mrs Tanqueray*, by ARTHUR WING PINERO

6 *Journey's End*, by R. C. SHERRIFF

7 *Tobacco Road*, by ERSKINE CALDWELL and JACK KIRKLAND

8 *Cavalcade*, by NOEL COWARD

9 *Life with Father*, by HOWARD LINDSAY and RUSSEL CROUSE

10 *Arsenic and Old Lace*, by JOSEPH KESSELRING

17 · Musicians in Literature

1 'Awakening up, he took her hollow *lute*,—tumultuous,—and, in chords that tenderest be, he played an ancient ditty. . . .'

2 'She'd git 'er little *banjo* an' she'd sing "Kulla-lo-lo"'

3 'He took up his *violin* from the corner, and as I stretched myself out he began to play some low, dreamy, melodious air—his own, no doubt, for he had a remarkable gift for improvisation.' *The Sign of the Four*, Chap. VIII

4 'The Owl looked up to the moon above, and sang to a small *guitar*'

5 'He thus confined himself upon the *guitar*. . . .'

6 'The ACTRESS is sitting at the *piano* playing Chopin's Nocturne in E flat'

7 '. . . the manifold music I build, bidding my *organ* obey . . .'

8 'Enter Nanki-Poo in great excitement. He carries a *guitar* on his back and a bundle of ballads in his hand.'

9 'Orpheus with his *lute* made trees, and the mountain tops that freeze, bow themselves when he did sing.' *Henry VIII*

10 'The Wedding-Guest here beat his breast, for he heard the loud *bassoon*.'

18 · Lies and Liars

1 *Tom Sawyer*, by MARK TWAIN

2 Pooh-Bah, in *The Mikado*, by W. S. GILBERT

3 Nora Helmer, in *A Doll's House*, by HENRIK IBSEN

4 *Baron Munchausen*, by RUDOLPH RASPE

5 Scarlet O'Hara Hamilton, in *Gone with the Wind*, by MARGARET MITCHELL

6 Mélisande, in *Pelléas et Mélisande*, by MAURICE MAETERLINCK

7 Colonel Jouve, in *The Siege of Berlin*, by ALPHONSE DAUDET

8 Joseph Jorkins, in *The Travel Tales of Joseph Jorkins*, by LORD DUNSANY

9 Vera Sappleton, in *The Open Window*, by SAKI

10 Ananias, *Acts V*

19 · Unique Combinations

1 *Ode to a Nightingale*, by KEATS

2 *To a Skylark*, by SHELLEY

3 *Upon Julia's Clothes*, by HERRICK

4 *To Althea from Prison*, by LOVELACE

5 *Ode on St Cecilia's Day*, by DRYDEN

6 *The Deserted Village*, by GOLD-SMITH

7 *Kubla Khan*, by COLERIDGE

8 *Sonnet CVI*, by SHAKESPEARE

9 *The Harlot's House*, by WILDE

10 *Waterloo*, by BYRON

11 *Dover Beach*, by MATTHEW ARNOLD

12 *I Wandered Lonely as a Cloud*, by WORDSWORTH

13 *Locksley Hall*, by TENNYSON

14 *Elegy Written in a Country Churchyard*, by GRAY

15 *Essay on Man*, by POPE

16 *Abou Ben Adhem*, by HUNT

17 *The Raven*, by POE

18 *Lycidas*, by MILTON

19 *The Song of the Shirt*, by HOOD

20 *Jabberwocky*, by CARROLL

20 · In the Nick of Time

1 *Jane Eyre*, by CHARLOTTE BRONTË

2 *The Last of the Mohicans*, by JAMES FENIMORE COOPER

3 *The Disappearance of Lady Frances Carfax*, by CONAN DOYLE

4 *The Three Musketeers*, by ALEXANDRE DUMAS

5 *Adam Bede*, by GEORGE ELIOT

6 *H.M.S. Pinafore*, by W. S. GILBERT

7 *Rage in Heaven*, by JAMES HILTON

8 *The Prisoner of Zenda*, by ANTHONY HOPE

9 *The Cloister and the Hearth*, by CHARLES READE

10 *Captain from Castile*, by SAMUEL SHELLABARGER

21 · Characters who Hid Themselves

1 John Ridd, in *Lorna Doone*, by RICHARD BLACKMORE

2 Lady Windermere, in *Lady Windermere's Fan*, by WILDE

3 Porphyro, in *The Eve of St Agnes*, by KEATS

4 Ginevra, by SAMUEL ROGERS

5 Frankenstein's monster, in *Frankenstein*, by MARY W. SHELLEY

6 Falstaff, in *The Merry Wives of Windsor*, by SHAKESPEARE

7 Tom Sawyer, by MARK TWAIN

8 Don Juan, by BYRON

9 Jim Hawkins, in *Treasure Island*, by ROBERT LOUIS STEVENSON

10 Gerard, in *The Cloister and the Hearth*, by CHARLES READE

22 · Sherlock Holmes

1 *A Study in Scarlet*

2 221-B Baker Street

3 Dr John H. Watson

4 Mrs Hudson

5 In the toe of a Persian slipper

6 Transfixed by a jack-knife into the centre of the wooden mantelpiece

7 Whisky-and-soda and a bit of lemon

8 Cocaine. (Possibly morphine also, if we can believe Dr Watson)

9 The violin

10 Medieval music

11 Pistol practice

12 The Diogenes Club

13 Mycroft Holmes

14 Professor Moriarty

15 The 'Gloria Scott' case

16 Bradstreet, Forbes, Gregson, Hill, Hopkins, Athelney Jones, Peter Jones, Lanner, Lestrade, MacDonald, MacKinnon, Merivale, Morton, Patterson, and Youghal

17 140

18 Irene Adler

19 Sussex Downs

20 Beekeeping

23 · Actors and Actresses

1 Snug, the Joiner, in *A Midsummer Night's Dream*, by SHAKESPEARE
2 Penrod Schofield, in *Penrod*, by BOOTH TARKINGTON
3 Emily Costigan, in *Pendennis*, by WILLIAM THACKERAY
4 The Actor, in *The Guardsman*, by FRANZ MOLNAR
5 Ninetta Crummles, the Infant Phenomenon, in *Nicholas Nickleby*, by DICKENS
6 Merton Gill, in *Merton of the Movies*, by HARRY LEON WILSON
7 Drury Lane, in *The Tragedy of X*, by BARNABY ROSS or ELLERY QUEEN
8 The Duke of Bilgewater, in *Huckleberry Finn*, by MARK TWAIN
9 *Zuleika Dobson*, by MAX BEERBOHM
10 *Bethel Merriday*, by SINCLAIR LEWIS

24 · Portable Equipment

1 Lennie Small, in *Of Mice and Men*, by JOHN STEINBECK
2 Brutus Jones, in *The Emperor Jones*, by EUGENE O'NEILL
3 Hyman Kaplan, in *The Education of Hyman Kaplan*, by LEONARD Q. ROSS
4 *Anthony Adverse*, by HERVEY ALLEN
5 Hans Castorp, in *The Magic Mountain*, by THOMAS MANN
6 Ah Sin, in *Plain Language from Truthful James*, by BRET HARTE
7 Peachey Carnahan, in *The Man Who Would be King*, by KIPLING
8 Aggie Pilkington, in *Tish*, by MARY ROBERTS RINEHART
9 The Old Man in the Corner, in the stories of BARONESS ORCZY
10 Captain Hook, in *Peter Pan*, by JAMES M. BARRIE

25 · Unusual First Names of Characters

1 Moncrieff	14 Babberly	27 Holmes	40 Baines
2 Everdene	15 Slappey	28 Wolfe	41 Whiteside
3 Thompson	16 Dishart	29 Carnahan	42 Forsyte
4 Little	17 Gabler	30 Sycamore	43 Judique
5 Sangrail	18 Poirot	31 Schofield	44 Carberry
6 Glencannon	19 Crane	32 Pickle	45 O'Ferrall
7 Topper	20 Lester	33 Whittier	46 Shandy
8 Stover	21 O'Hara	34 Fogg	47 Heep
9 Troop	22 Doone	35 Crawley	48 Squeers
10 Jessup	23 Lescault	36 Bunthorne	49 Micawber
11 Dantes	24 Falcone	37 Butler	50 Cravat
12 Grangerford	25 Cheevy	38 Crusoe	51 Dobson
13 Arden	26 Flanders	39 Panza	

26 · Famous Animals

1 *Peter Rabbit*, by BEATRIX POTTER
2 *Bambi*, by FELIX SALTEN
3 Djali, in *The Hunchback of Notre Dame*, by VICTOR HUGO

98

4 Mignonette, in *A Passion in the Desert*, by BALZAC
5 Oscar, in *Chad Hanna*, by WALTER D. EDMONDS
6 Babe, from the Paul Bunyan legends, collected by JAMES STEVENS

7 *Ferdinand*, by MUNRO LEAF
8 The Empress of Blandings, in *Fish Preferred*, by P. G. WODEHOUSE
9 Mehitabel, in *Archy and Mehitabel*, by DON MARQUIS
10 *Sredni Vashtar*, by SAKI

27 · Four-word Quotations

1 *Sonnet XXX*, by SHAKESPEARE
2 *Ode to a Nightingale*, by KEATS
3 *The Lay of the Last Minstrel*, by SCOTT
4 *Jabberwocky*, by CARROLL
5 *The Ancient Mariner*, by COLERIDGE
6 *Maud Muller*, by WHITTIER
7 *The Ladies*, by KIPLING
8 *Patterns*, by LOWELL
9 *Ode to the West Wind*, by SHELLEY
10 *Sir Galahad*, by TENNYSON
11 *America*, by SMITH

12 *Jenny Kiss'd Me*, by HUNT
13 *I Wandered Lonely as a Cloud*, by WORDSWORTH
14 *Why So Pale and Wan?* by SUCKLING
15 *Annabel Lee*, by POE
16 *The Rubáiyát*, by FITZGERALD
17 *The Owl and the Pussycat*, by LEAR
18 *The Battle of Blenheim*, by SOUTHEY
19 *Lycidas*, by MILTON
20 *Paul Revere's Ride*, by LONGFELLOW

28 · Doctors in Literature

1 Henry Faust, in *Faust*, by GOETHE
2 Dr Sangrado, in *Gil Blas*, by RENÉ LESAGE
3 Lemuel Gulliver, in *Gulliver's Travels*, by JONATHAN SWIFT
4 Victor Frankenstein, in *Frankenstein*, by MARY SHELLEY
5 Dr Manette, in *A Tale of Two Cities*, by DICKENS
6 Sir Colenso Ridgeon, in *The Doctor's Dilemma*, by GEORGE BERNARD SHAW
7 Dr Heidegger, in *Dr Heidegger's Experiment*, by NATHANIEL HAWTHORNE
8 Dr Jekyll, in *Dr Jekyll and Mr Hyde*, by R. L. STEVENSON
9 Dr John H. Watson, in *A Study in Scarlet*, by CONAN DOYLE
10 *Arrowsmith*, by SINCLAIR LEWIS

29 Characters Concerned with Bridges

1 *Horatius*, by THOMAS MACAULAY
2 Robert Jordan, in *For Whom the Bell Tolls*, by ERNEST HEMINGWAY
3 Peyton Farquhar, in *An Occurrence at Owl Creek Bridge*, by AMBROSE BIERCE
4 Brother Juniper, in *The Bridge of San Luis Ray*, by THORNTON WILDER

5 Phileas Fogg, in *Around the World in Eighty Days*, by JULES VERNE
6 *Lucy Gray*, by WORDSWORTH
7 Sherlock Holmes, in *Thor Bridge*, by CONAN DOYLE
8 Nancy, in *Oliver Twist*, by DICKENS
9 *Robin Hood*
10 *Chad Hanna*, by WALTER EDMONDS

30 · Money in Literature

1. Antonio, in *The Merchant of Venice*, by SHAKESPEARE
2. *The Pied Piper of Hamelin*, by ROBERT BROWNING
3. *Silas Marner*, by GEORGE ELIOT
4. Mr Wilkins Micawber, in *David Copperfield*, by DICKENS
5. Della Young, in *The Gift of the Magi*, by O. HENRY
6. Kate Sims, in *The Twelve Pound Look*, by JAMES M. BARRIE
7. Mr White, in *The Monkey's Paw*, by W. W. JACOBS
8. M. Loisel, in *The Necklace*, by GUY DE MAUPASSANT
9. Keawe, in *The Bottle Imp*, by R. L. STEVENSON
10. Montgomery Brewster, in *Brewsters Millions*, by GEORGE BARR MCCUTCHEON

31 · Some Interrupted Weddings

1. *Romeo and Juliet*, by SHAKESPEARE
2. *The Cloister and the Hearth*, by CHARLES READE
3. *Frankenstein*, by MARY SHELLEY
4. *Jane Eyre*, by CHARLOTTE BRONTË
5. *Lochinvar*, by SCOTT
6. *Lorna Doone*, by RICHARD BLACKMORE
7. *The Adventure of the Noble Client*, by CONAN DOYLE
8. *Great Expectations*, by DICKENS
9. *A Comedy in Rubber*, by O. HENRY
10. *Waiting at the Church*, by FRED W. LEIGH

32 · First Lines of Famous Poems

1. *The Faery Queene*, by SPENSER
2. *The Barefoot Boy*, by WHITTIER
3. *The Man with the Hoe*, by MARKHAM
4. *The Passionate Shepherd to His Love*, by MARLOWE
5. *Ode on St Cecilia's Day*, by POPE
6. *Sonnet Composed upon Westminster Bridge*, by WORDSWORTH
7. *Goodbye*, by EMERSON
8. *Il Penseroso*, by MILTON
9. *Let the Toast Pass*, by SHERIDAN
10. *The Old Familiar Faces*, by LAMB
11. *Ozymandias*, by SHELLEY
12. *Annabel Lee*, by POE
13. *The Patriot*, by BROWNING
14. *Jenny Kiss'd Me*, by HUNT
15. *On First Looking into Chapman's Homer*, by KEATS
16. *The Deserted Village*, by GOLDSMITH
17. *Tears, Idle Tears*, by TENNYSON
18. *To Lucasta, Going to the Wars*, by LOVELACE
19. *The Destruction of Sennacherib*, by BYRON
20. *Why So Pale and Wan?* by SUCKLING

33 · Who is She ?

1. Susan, in *Sweet William's Farewell to Black-eyed Susan*, by JOHN GAY
2. *The Solitary Reaper*, by WORDSWORTH
3. Madeline, in *The Eve of St Agnes*, by KEATS
4. *The Beggar Maid*, by TENNYSON
5. *Christabel*, by COLERIDGE

6 Belinda, in *The Rape of the Lock*, by ALEXANDER POPE

7 Lucy, in *She Dwelt Among the Untrodden Ways*, by WORDSWORTH

8 Silvia, in *Who is Silvia?* by SHAKESPEARE

9 *La Belle Dame Sans Merci*, by KEATS

10 *My Last Duchess*, by ROBERT BROWNING

11 *The Blessed Damozel*, by D. G. ROSSETTI

12 The rich attorney's daughter, in *Trial by Jury*, by W. S. GILBERT

13 Ellen Netherby, in *Lochinvar*, by SCOTT

14 Porphyria, in *Porphyria's Lover*, by ROBERT BROWNING

15 *Mariana*, by TENNYSON

16 *Ruth*, by THOMAS HOOD

17 *Maud Muller*, by JOHN GREENLEAF WHITTIER

18 The skipper's daughter, in *The Wreck of the Hesperus*, by LONGFELLOW

19 *Annabel Lee*, by POE

20 Charlotte, in *The Sorrows of Werther*, by WILLIAM THACKERAY

34 · Twice-married Men

1 Stephen Haines, in *The Women*, by CLARE BOOTHE

2 *Arrowsmith*, by SINCLAIR LEWIS

3 *David Copperfield*, by DICKENS

4 Edward Rochester, in *Jane Eyre*, by CHARLOTTE BRONTË

5 *Anthony Adverse*, by HERVEY ALLEN

6 Archibald Carlyle, in *East Lynne*, by MRS. HENRY WOOD

7 Godfrey Cass, in *Silas Marner*, by GEORGE ELIOT

8 Harry Sims, in *The Twelve Pound Look*, by JAMES M. BARRIE

9 Aubrey Tanqueray, in *The Second Mrs Tanqueray*, by ARTHUR WING PINERO

10 Soames Forsyte, in *The Forsyte Saga*, by JOHN GALSWORTHY

35 · Unusual Hiding Places

1 *Silas Marner*, by GEORGE ELIOT

2 Scarlett O'Hara, in *Gone With the Wind*, by MARGARET MITCHELL

3 Becky Sharp, in *Vanity Fair*, by WILLIAM THACKERAY

4 Auguste Dupin, in *The Purloined Letter*, by POE

5 Sherlock Holmes, in *The Adventure of the Six Napoleons*, by CONAN DOYLE

6 Tom Canty, in *The Prince and the Pauper*, by MARK TWAIN

7 Isabella, in *The Pot of Basil*, by KEATS

8 Captain Elisha Jorham, in *Anthony Adverse*, by HERVEY ALLEN

9 Rosanna Spearman, in *The Moonstone*, by WILKIE COLLINS

10 Don Birnham, in *The Lost Week-End*, by CHARLES JACKSON

36 · 'The Face is Familiar . . .'

1 Gavin Dishart

2 Marian Forrester

3 Anne Catherick

4 James Wait

5 Natty Bumppo

6 Renny Whiteoak

7 John Harmon

8 Edmond Dantes

9 Soames Forsyte

10 Charles Primrose

11 Philip Nolan

12 Michael Henchard

13 Jeff Peters	20 Jody Baxter
14 Rudolph	21 Ellen Douglas
15 Quasimodo	22 Antonio
16 Sheridan Whiteside	23 Daniel Pike
17 Daniel Dravot	24 Hank Morgan
18 Sam Small	25 George Fotheringay
19 Clem Hawley	

37 · Familiar Lines of Famous Poems

1 'Ah, make the most of what we yet may spend.' FITZGERALD

2 'Blessings on thee, little man.' WHITTIER

3 'Breathes there the man with soul so dead.' SCOTT

4 'Bright star! would I were steadfast as thou art.' KEATS

5 'Come live with me and be my love.' MARLOWE

6 'Descend, ye Nine! descend and sing.' POPE

7 'Far from the madding crowd's ignoble strife.' GRAY

8 'Flow gently, sweet Afton, among thy green braes.' BURNS

9 'Full fathom five thy father lies.' SHAKESPEARE

10 'Great rats, small rats, lean rats, brawny rats.' BROWNING

11 'How doth the little busy bee improve each shining hour?' WATTS

12 'In Xanadu did Kubla Khan a stately pleasure-dome decree.' COLERIDGE

13 'I wandered lonely as a cloud.' WORDSWORTH

14 'Little Lamb, who made thee?' BLAKE

15 'My strength is as the strength of ten.' TENNYSON

16 'Once upon a midnight dreary.' POE

17 'O wild West Wind, thou breath of Autumn's being.' SHELLEY

18 'She walks in beauty, like the night.' BYRON

19 'The blessed damozel leaned out from the gold bar of heaven.' ROSSETTI

20 ''Twas brillig, and the slithy toves did gyre and gimble in the wabe.' LEWIS CARROLL

21 ''Twas many and many a year ago.' POE

22 'Whan that Aprille with his shoures soote.' CHAUCER

23 'Whenas in silks my Julia goes.' HERRICK

24 'When lilacs last in the dooryard bloomed.' WHITMAN

25 'With fingers weary and worn, with eyelids heavy and red.' HOOD.

38 · Transportation in Fiction

1 *Sindbad the Sailor*, in *The Arabian Nights*

2 *Lohengrin*, by WAGNER

3 *Daedalus and Icarus*, in Greek Mythology

4 *The Jumblies*, by EDWARD LEAR

5 Prince Dolor, in *The Little Lame Prince*, by DINAH MARIA MULOCK CRAIK

6 Phileas Fogg, in *Around the World in Eighty Days*, by JULES VERNE

7 *Pinocchio*, by CARLO COLLODI

8 *Wynken, Blynken, and Nod*, by EUGENE FIELD

9 *Cinderella*, by CHARLES PERRAULT

10 Lemuel Gulliver, in *Gulliver's Travels*, by JONATHAN SWIFT

102

39 · Alice in Wonderland

1 Alice
2 The Dodo
3 The March Hare
4 The Queen of Hearts
5 The Duchess
6 The Mock Turtle
7 The Queen of Hearts
8 The Tiger Lily
9 The Red Queen
10 The Gnat

11 Tweedledum
12 The Walrus
13 The White Queen
14 The White Queen
15 Humpty Dumpty
16 The White King
17 Haigha
18 The Unicorn
19 The White Knight
20 The Red Queen

40 · Songs and Their Singers

1 Johnny Nolan, in *A Tree Grows in Brooklyn*, by BETTY SMITH
2 Billy Bones, in *Treasure Island*, by ROBERT LOUIS STEVENSON
3 Porphyro, in *The Eve of St Agnes*, by KEATS
4 *Trilby*, by GEORGE DU MAURIER
5 The White Knight, in *Through the Looking Glass*, by LEWIS CARROLL
6 Jane Champion, in *The Rosary*, by FLORENCE BARCLAY

7 Tony Lumpkin, in *She Stoops to Conquer*, by GOLDSMITH
8 Pippa, in *Pippa Passes*, by ROBERT BROWNING
9 Ariel, in *The Tempest*, by SHAKESPEARE
10 Olivia Primrose, in *The Vicar of Wakefield*, by GOLDSMITH

41 · A Patchwork Poem

1 *I Wandered Lonely as a Cloud*, by WORDSWORTH
2 *The Lady of the Lake*, by SCOTT
3 *Annabel Lee*, by POE
4 *Christabel*, by COLERIDGE
5 *She Was a Phantom of Delight*, by WORDSWORTH
6 *She Was a Phantom of Delight*, by WORDSWORTH
7 *La Belle Dame Sans Merci*, by KEATS
8 *The Blessed Damozel*, by D. G. ROSSETTI
9 *Trees*, by KILMER

10 *The Deacon's Masterpiece*, by HOLMES
11 *Jacqueline*, by ROGERS
12 *The Beggar Maid*, by TENNYSON
13 *Upon Julia's Clothes*, by HERRICK
14 *The Lay of the Last Minstrel*, by SCOTT
15 *Go, Lovely Rose*, by WALLER
16 *Jabberwocky*, by LEWIS CARROLL
17 *In Memoriam*, by TENNYSON
18 *I Do Not Love Thee, Dr Fell*, by BROWN
19 *Alice Gray*, by MEE
20 *Christabel*, by COLERIDGE

42 · Statues in Literature

1 *Julius Caesar*, by SHAKESPEARE
2 *Horatius*, by THOMAS MACAULAY

3 *Our Lady's Juggler*, by ANATOLE FRANCE

4 *The Old Curiosity Shop*, by DICKENS
5 *Don Giovanni*, by LORENZO DA PONTE
6 *Ozymandias*, by SHELLEY
7 *Anthony Adverse*, by HERVEY ALLEN

8 *The Wrong Box*, by ROBERT LOUIS STEVENSON
9 *Sappho*, by ALPHONSE DAUDET
10 *The Bishop's Move* (from *Meet Mr Mulliner*), by P. G. WODEHOUSE

43 · Elopers in Literature

1 Jessica and Lorenzo, in *The Merchant of Venice*, by SHAKESPEARE
2 Olivia Primrose and Mr Thornhill, in *The Vicar of Wakefield*, by GOLDSMITH
3 Lord Ullin's daughter and the chief of Ulva's isle, in *Lord Ullin's Daughter*, by THOMAS CAMPBELL
4 Porphyro and Madeline, in *The Eve of St Agnes*, by KEATS
5 Lochinvar and Ellen Netherby, in *Lochinvar*, by SCOTT
6 Sophia Grangerford and Harney

Shepherdson, in *Huckleberry Finn*, by MARK TWAIN
7 George Osborne and Amelia Sedley, in *Vanity Fair*, by WILLIAM THACKERAY
8 Lydia Bennet and Mr Wickham in *Pride and Prejudice*, by JANE AUSTEN
9 Little Emily and James Steerforth, in *David Copperfield*, by DICKENS
10 Sophia Baines and Gerald Scales, in *The Old Wives' Tale*, by ARNOLD BENNETT

44 · Criminals in Literature

1 Black Michael, Lord of Zenda, in *The Prisoner of Zenda*, by ANTHONY HOPE
2 Bo-Bo and Ho-Ti, in *A Dissertation on Roast Pig*, by CHARLES LAMB
3 Philip Nolan, in *The Man Without a Country*, by EDWARD EVERETT HALE
4 Hester Prynne, in *The Scarlet Letter*, by NATHANIEL HAWTHORNE
5 Jack Dawkins, the Artful Dodger, in *Oliver Twist*, by DICKENS

6 Jeff Peters, in *The Gentle Grafter*, by O. HENRY
7 John Silver, in *Treasure Island*, by ROBERT LOUIS STEVENSON
8 Romeo, in *Romeo and Juliet*, by Shakespeare
9 Ko-Ko, in *The Mikado*, by W. S. GILBERT
10 Dunstan Cass, in *Silas Marner*, by GEORGE ELIOT

45 · Characters Who had Unusual Powers

1 *Dracula*, by BRAM STOKER
2 Mephistopheles, in *Faust*, by GOETHE
3 Rima, in *Green Mansions*, by W. H. HUDSON
4 *Peter Ibbetson*, by GEORGE DU MAURIER

5 Beatrice, in *Rappaccini's Daughter*, by HAWTHORNE
6 *Dr Jekyll and Mr Hyde*, by ROBERT LOUIS STEVENSON
7 Sam Small, in *The Flying Yorkshireman*, by ERIC KNIGHT

8 Father Perrault, in *Lost Horizon*, by JAMES HILTON

9 George Fotheringay, in *The Man Who Could Work Miracles*, by H. G. WELLS

10 Hiawatha, in *The Song of Hiawatha*, by LONGFELLOW

46 · Famous Soldiers

1 Major General Stanley, in *The Pirates of Penzance*, by W. S. GILBERT

2 Captain George Osborne, in *Vanity Fair*, by WILLIAM THACKERAY

3 Uncle Toby, in *Tristram Shandy*, by LAURENCE STERNE

4 Ben Battle, in *Faithless Nelly Gray*, by THOMAS HOOD

5 Lieutenant Austin Limmason, in *The Man Who Was*, by RUDYARD KIPLING

6 Rhett Butler, in *Gone with the Wind*, by MARGARET MITCHELL

7 Henry Fleming, in *The Red Badge of Courage*, by STEPHEN CRANE

8 Victor Joppolo, in *A Bell for Adano*, by JOHN HERSEY

9 Denys, in *The Cloister and the Hearth*, by CHARLES READE

10 *Danny Deever*, by KIPLING

47 · Numbers in Titles

a Three	**f** Seven	**k** Three	**p** Ten
b Twenty	**g** Thirty-nine	**l** Three	**q** Two
c Eight	**h** Two	**m** 20,000	**r** 1,000,000
d Seven	**i** 1919	**n** Seven	**s** 20,000
e Twelve	**j** Twenty	**o** Six	**t** Forty

48 · Lines that Precede Famous Lines

1 'A brute I might have been, but would not sink i' the scale.' BROWNING

2 'Flow gently, sweet Afton, disturb not her dream.' BURNS

3 'On with the dance! Let joy be unconfined.' BYRON

4 'A sadder and a wiser man he rose the morrow morn.' COLERIDGE

5 'I have been faithful to thee, Cynara, in my fashion.' DOWSON

6 'Ah, take the Cash, and let the Credit go.' FITZGERALD

7 'And fools who came to scoff remained to pray.' GOLDSMITH

8 'The paths of glory lead but to the grave.' GRAY

9 'I am the master of my fate: I am the captain of my soul.' HENLEY

10 'Say I'm growing old, but add: Jenny kissed me.' HUNT

11 'An' they're hangin' Danny Deever in the morning.' KIPLING

12 'One, if by land, and two, if by sea.' LONGFELLOW

13 'They also serve who only stand and wait.' MILTON

14 'I'll come to thee by moonlight though hell should bar the way!' NOYES

15 'The proper study of mankind is man.' POPE

16 'They'll have fleet steeds that follow, quoth young Lochinvar.' SCOTT

17 'Thou art more lovely and more temperate.' SHAKESPEARE

18 'Our sweetest songs are those that tell of saddest thought.' SHELLEY

19 'But 'twas a famous victory.' SOUTHEY

20 'In the spring a young man's fancy lightly turns to thoughts of love.' TENNYSON

49 · A Mother Goose Quiz

1 Little Johnny Green
2 The flute
3 He caught fishes in other men's ditches
4 Whale
5 Welshman
6 Vinegar and brown paper
7 Curly Locks
8 A night gown
9 A spider
10 Broth without any bread
11 *Twee-tweedle-dee*, *tweedle-dee*, went the fiddlers

12 And what they could not eat that night the queen next morning fried.
13 Saturday
14 Tarts
15 Four-and-twenty
16 You shall dine on cherry pie and drink currant wine
17 No pie
18 To sea
19 A pig
20 Noon

50 · Ten Famous Detectives

1 Auguste Dupin, by POE
2 Father Brown, by G. K. CHESTERTON
3 Sherlock Holmes, by CONAN DOYLE
4 Charlie Chan, by EARL DERR BIGGERS
5 Philo Vance, by S. S. VAN DINE

6 Hercule Poirot, by AGATHA CHRISTIE
7 Sergeant Cuff, by WILKIE COLLINS
8 Lord Peter Wimsey, by DOROTHY SAYERS
9 Nero Wolfe, by REX STOUT
10 Ellery Queen, by ELLERY QUEEN

51 · Place Names in Poetry

1 BURNS	9 SCOTT
2 GOLDSMITH	10 CANNING
3 MILLER	11 C. E. CARRYL
4 SOUTHEY	12 BROWNING
5 BYRON	13 NOYES
6 LINDSAY	14 HOUSMAN
7 WORDSWORTH	15 KIPLING
8 LONGFELLOW	16 FITZGERALD

17 ARNOLD	25 ROBINSON
18 WILDE	26 GILBERT
19 FLECKER	27 COWPER
20 TENNYSON	28 COLERIDGE
21 CHAUCER	29 POE
22 MASTERS	30 LEAR
23 FOSTER	
24 MOORE	

52 · Shakespeare's Opening Lines

1 Antonio, in *The Merchant of Venice*
2 The first witch, in *Macbeth*
3 Flavius, in *Julius Caesar*
4 Orsino, in *Twelfth Night*
5 Theseus, in *Midsummer Night's Dream*
6 Earl of Kent, in *King Lear*
7 Richard, Duke of Gloster, in *Richard III*
8 Henry, in *Henry IV, 1*
9 Ferdinand, in *Love's Labour's Lost*
10 Duke of Bedford, in *Henry VI, 1*

53 · Characters who Were Shipwrecked

1 *Robinson Crusoe*, by DANIEL DEFOE
2 *Enoch Arden*, by ALFRED TENNYSON
3 Lemuel Gulliver, in *A Voyage to Lilliput*, by JONATHAN SWIFT
4 *Don Juan*, by BYRON
5 Prospero, in *The Tempest*, by SHAKESPEARE
6 William Crichton, in *The Admirable Crichton*, by JAMES M. BARRIE
7 Ishmael, in *Moby Dick*, by HERMAN MELVILLE
8 Robinson Crusoe, in *Robinson Crusoe's Story*, by CHARLES EDWARD CARRYL
9 Mr Royle, in *The Wreck of the Grosvenor*, by CLARK RUSSELL
10 Marlow, in *Youth*, by JOSEPH CONRAD

54 · Poets in Literature

1 Reginald Bunthorne, in *Patience*, by W. S. GILBERT
2 Orlando, in *As You Like It*, by SHAKESPEARE
3 Petit the Poet, in *Spoon River Anthology*, by EDGAR LEE MASTERS
4 Sir Benjamin Backbite, in *A School for Scandal*, by SHERIDAN
5 Eden Whiteoak, in *The Master of Jalna*, by MAZO DE LA ROCHE
6 Willie Baxter, in *Seventeen*, by BOOTH TARKINGTON
7 Eugene Marchbanks in *Candida*, by GEORGE BERNARD SHAW
8 Mrs Leo Hunter, in *Pickwick Papers*, by DICKENS
9 Emmeline Grangerford, in *Huckleberry Finn*, by MARK TWAIN
10 Archie, in *Archie and Mehitabel*, by DON MARQUIS

55 · Famous Ghost Stories

1 Jacob Marley, in *A Christmas Carol*, by DICKENS
2 Mrs Wessington, in *The Phantom Rickshaw*, by KIPLING
3 *The Apparition of Mrs Veal*, by DANIEL DEFOE
4 Charles Condomine, in *Blithe Spirit*, by NOEL COWARD
5 Marion Kerby, in *Topper*, by THORNE SMITH
6 Peter Quint and Miss Jessel, in *The Turn of the Screw*, by HENRY JAMES
7 Hamlet's father, in *Hamlet*, by SHAKESPEARE
8 The girl, in *The Furnished Room*, by O. HENRY
9 *The Inexperienced Ghost*, by H. G. WELLS
10 Sir Simon de Canterville, in *The Canterville Ghost*, by WILDE

56 · Fiction's Famous Funerals

1 Henry Leek, in *Buried Alive*, by ARNOLD BENNETT

2 Tom Sawyer, in *The Adventures of Tom Sawyer*, by MARK TWAIN

3 Sherlock Holmes, in *The Disappearance of Lady Frances Carfax*, by CONAN DOYLE

4 Adeline Whiteoak, in *The Whiteoaks of Jalna*, by MAZO DE LA ROCHE

5 Abby and Martha Brewster, in *Arsenic and Old Lace*, by JOSEPH KESSELRING

6 Michael Geste, in *Beau Geste*, by P. C. WREN

7 Emily Gibbs, in *Our Town*, by THORNTON WILDER

8 Sam McGee, in *The Cremation of Sam McGee*, by ROBERT W. SERVICE

9 Johnny Nolan, in *A Tree Grows in Brooklyn*, by BETTY SMITH

10 Jud Fry, in *Oklahoma!* by RICHARD RODGERS and OSCAR HAMMERSTEIN II

57 · Twenty Famous Pen Names

1 BRONTË
2 MILLAY
3 DICKENS
4 DODGSON
5 LAMB
6 EVANS
7 THIBAULT
8 BAKER
9 PORTER
10 VIAUD
11 BULWER-LYTTON
12 MACPHERSON
13 DE LA RAMÉE
14 MUNRO
15 DUDEVANT
16 STEIN
17 CLEMENS
18 WRIGHT
19 AROUET
20 BROWNE

58 · Artists in Literature

1 Traddles, in *David Copperfield*, by DICKENS

2 Little Billee (William Bagot), in *Trilby*, by GEORGE DU MAURIER

3 The Saint, in the stories by LESLIE CHARTERIS

4 Dick Heldar, in *The Light That Failed*, by KIPLING

5 Old Behrman, in *The Last Leaf*, by O. HENRY

6 Penelope Sycamore, in *You Can't Take It With You*, by GEORGE KAUFMAN and MOSS HART

7 Charles Strickland, in *The Moon and Sixpence*, by SOMERSET MAUGHAM

8 Basil Hallward, in *The Picture of Dorian Gray*, by WILDE

9 Louis Dubedat, in *The Doctor's Dilemma*, by GEORGE BERNARD SHAW

10 Emmeline Grangerford, in *Huckleberry Finn*, by MARK TWAIN

59 · Brothers and Sisters

1 Sawyer, in *The Adventures of Tom Sawyer*, by MARK TWAIN

2 Ridd, in *Lorna Doone*, by RICHARD BLACKMORE

3 Geste, in *Beau Geste*, by P. C. WREN

4 Darling, in *Peter Pan*, by JAMES M. BARRIE

5 O'Hara, in *Gone with the Wind*, by MARGARET MITCHELL

6 Nolan, in *A Tree Grows in Brooklyn*, by BETTY SMITH

7 March, in *Little Women*, by LOUISA M. ALCOTT

8 Robinson, in *Swiss Family Robinson*, by JOHANN WYSS

9 Macauley, in *The Human Comedy*, by WILLIAM SAROYAN

10 Primrose, in *The Vicar of Wakefield*, by GOLDSMITH

11 Stanley, in *The Pirates of Penzance*, by W. S. GILBERT

12 Pepper, in *The Five Little Peppers*, by MARGARET SIDNEY

13 Bennet, in *Pride and Prejudice*, by JANE AUSTEN

14 Wiggs, in *Mrs Wiggs of the Cabbage Patch*, by ALICE HEGAN RICE

15 Joad, in *The Grapes of Wrath*, by JOHN STEINBECK

16 Whiteoak, in *Jalna*, by MAZO DE LA ROCHE

17 Eliasson, in *The Cloister and the Hearth*, by CHARLES READE

18 Moulton-Barrett, in *The Barretts of Wimpole Street*, by RUDOLF BESIER

19 Forsyte, in *The Forsyte Saga*, by JOHN GALSWORTHY

20 Guessippi, in *Anthony Adverse*, by HERVEY ALLEN

60 · Clocks and Watches

1 *Tristram Shandy*, by LAURENCE STERNE

2 Jim Young, in *The Gift of the Magi*, by O. HENRY

3 The Mad Hatter, in *Alice in Wonderland*, by LEWIS CARROLL

4 Dunstan Cass, in *Silas Marner*, by GEORGE ELIOT

5 Walter Burns, in *The Front Page*, by BEN HECHT and CHARLES MACARTHUR

6 Miss Havisham, in *Great Expectations*, by DICKENS

7 Captain Cuttle, in *Dombey and Son*, by DICKENS

8 Sherlock Holmes, in *The Sign of the Four*, by CONAN DOYLE

9 Mr Josser, in *Dulcimer Street*, by NORMAN COLLINS

10 Phineas Fogg, in *Around the World in Eighty Days*, by JULES VERNE

61 · It Could Happen to You !

1 Pyecraft, in *The Truth about Pyecraft*, by H. G. WELLS

2 *Rip Van Winkle*, by WASHINGTON IRVING

3 Juliet, in *Romeo and Juliet*, by SHAKESPEARE

4 Dr Heidegger, in *Dr Heidegger's Experiment*, by NATHANIEL HAWTHORNE

5 Dr Jekyll, in *Dr Jekyll and Mr Hyde*, by ROBERT LOUIS STEVENSON

6 *Snow White*, by THE GRIMM BROTHERS

7 Persephone, in Greek Mythology

8 Circe, in *The Odyssey*, by HOMER

9 Lucius Apuleius, in *The Golden Ass*, by APULEIUS

10 Alice, in *Alice in Wonderland*, by LEWIS CARROLL

62 · Aspects of Nature in Poetry

1 *The Lake Isle of Innisfree*, by YEATS

2 *I Shall Go Back*, by MILLAY

3 *Il Penseroso*, by MILTON

4 *Break, Break, Break*, by TENNYSON

5 *Dover Beach,* by MATTHEW ARNOLD
6 *Stopping by Woods on a Snowy Evening,* by FROST
7 *To a Waterfowl,* by BRYANT
8 *The Merchant of Venice,* by SHAKES-PEARE
9 *Elegy Written in a Country Churchyard,* by GRAY
10 *She Dwelt among the Untrodden Ways,* by WORDSWORTH
11 *Evangeline,* by LONGFELLOW
12 *Sweet Afton,* by BURNS

13 *Childe Harold's Pilgrimage,* by BYRON
14 *Ode to a Nightingale,* by KEATS
15 *Love Among the Ruins,* by BROWNING
16 *The Landing of the Pilgrim Fathers,* by HEMANS
17 *Give Me the Splendid Silent Sun,* by WHITMAN
18 *Hohenlinden,* by CAMPBELL
19 *The Ancient Mariner,* by COLERIDGE
20 *Ode to the West Wind,* by SHELLEY

63 · The Sailor's Life

1 *Captain Reece,* by W. S. GILBERT
2 *The Odyssey,* by HOMER
3 *H.M.S. Pinafore,* by W. S. GILBERT
4 *Ben Hur,* by LEW WALLACE
5 *The Yarn of the Nancy Bell,* by W. S. GILBERT
6 *The Ancient Mariner,* by COLERIDGE

7 *The Walloping Window-Blind,* by CHARLES EDWARD CARRYL
8 *The Hunting of the Snark,* by LEWIS CARROLL
9 *MS. Found in a Bottle,* by POE
10 *The Ballad of the Billycock,* by ANTHONY DEANE

64 · Memorable Words of Dickens Characters

1 Wilkins Micawber
2 Tony Weller
3 Jonas Chuzzlewit
4 Sairey Gamp
5 Mrs General
6 Alfred Mantalini
7 Mrs Gummidge
8 Uriah Heep

9 Captain Cuttle
10 Mark Tapley
11 Mr Barkis
12 Jerry Cruncher
13 Oliver Twist
14 Dick Swiveller
15 Thomas Gradgrind

65 · Chapter Headings

1 *The Forsyte Saga,* by JOHN GALSWORTHY
2 *Beau Geste,* by P. C. WREN
3 *Anthony Adverse,* by HERVEY ALLEN
4 *Jalna,* by MAZO DE LA ROCHE
5 *Far from the Madding Crowd,* by THOMAS HARDY
6 *Vanity Fair,* by WILLIAM THACKERAY
7 *David Copperfield,* by DICKENS
8 *The Prisoner of Zenda,* by ANTHONY HOPE

9 *The Connecticut Yankee,* by MARK TWAIN
10 *Black Beauty,* by ANNA SEWELL
11 *Tom Sawyer,* by MARK TWAIN
12 *Pendennis,* by WILLIAM THACKERAY
13 *Lorna Doone,* by RICHARD BLACKMORE
14 *The Sign of the Four,* by CONAN DOYLE
15 *The Hunchback of Notre Dame,* by VICTOR HUGO
16 *Candide,* by VOLTAIRE

17 *The Vicar of Wakefield*, by GOLD-
SMITH
18 *The Human Comedy*, by WILLIAM
SAROYAN
19 *The Three Musketeers*, by ALEX-
ANDRE DUMAS

20 *Little Women*, by LOUISA M. ALCOTT
21 *Treasure Island*, by ROBERT LOUIS
STEVENSON
22 *Through the Looking Glass*, by
LEWIS CARROLL

66 · Titles Taken from Shakespeare

1 *Romeo and Juliet*
2 *Julius Caesar*
3 *Macbeth*
4 *Macbeth*
5 *Richard II*
6 *Twelfth Night*
7 *As You Like It*
8 *The Tempest*
9 *A Midsummer Night's Dream*
10 *Hamlet*

11 *As You Like It*
12 *King John*
13 *The Tempest*
14 *Macbeth*
15 *Twelfth Night*
16 *Romeo and Juliet*
17 *Sonnet XXX*
18 *Macbeth*
19 *Hamlet*
20 *Hamlet*

67 · How well-known Novels End

1 *The Good Earth*, by PEARL BUCK
2 *Rebecca*, by DAPHNE DU MAURIER
3 *The Vicar of Wakefield*, by GOLD-
SMITH
4 *Gone with the Wind*, by MARGARET
MITCHELL
5 *The Picture of Dorian Gray*, by
WILDE

6 *Silas Marner*, by GEORGE ELIOT
7 *Vanity Fair*, by WILLIAM THACK-
ERAY
8 *The Old Wives' Tale*, by ARNOLD
BENNETT
9 *Arrowsmith*, by SINCLAIR LEWIS
10 *The Sign of the Four*, by CONAN
DOYLE

68 · I Felt Such a Fool!

1 Mr Pickwick, in *Pickwick Papers*,
by DICKENS
2 *Tom Sawyer*, by MARK TWAIN
3 Ernest Pontifex, in *The Way of
All Flesh*, by SAMUEL BUTLER
4 Becky Sharp, in *Vanity Fair*, by
WILLIAM THACKERAY
5 John Gilpin, in *John Gilpin's Ride*,
by WILLIAM COWPER

6 Strephon, in *Iolanthe*, by W. S.
GILBERT
7 Mr Pim, in *Mr Pim Passes By*, by
A. A. MILNE
8 George Mulliner, in *The Truth
About George*, by P. G. WODEHOUSE
9 *Elmer Gantry*, by SINCLAIR LEWIS
10 Walter Bidlake, in *Point Counter
Point*, by ALDOUS HUXLEY

69 · First Words of Famous Quatrains

1 *She Dwelt among the Untrodden
Ways*, by WORDSWORTH

2 *The Rubáiyát of Omar Khayyám*,
by FITZGERALD

3 *The Tiger*, by BLAKE

4 *To Celia*, by JONSON

5 *Elegy Written in a Country Churchyard*, by GRAY

6 *Flow Gently, Sweet Afton*, by BURNS

7 *To the Virgins*, by HERRICK

8 *Resumé*, by PARKER

9 *A Psalm of Life*, by LONGFELLOW

10 *Loveliest of Trees*, by A. E. HOUSMAN

11 *Maid of Athens*, by BYRON

12 *To ——*, by SHELLEY

13 *Invictus*, by HENLEY

14 *Jenny Kiss'd Me*, by HUNT

15 *To Althea from Prison*, by LOVELACE

16 *The Kiss*, by TEASDALE

17 *Crossing the Bar*, by TENNYSON

18 *The Bridge of Sighs*, by HOOD

70 · Characters and Windows

1 *Barbara Freitchie*, by JOHN GREENLEAF WHITTIER

2 *The Lady of Shalott*, by TENNYSON

3 Mélisande, in *Pelléas et Mélisande*, by MAURICE MAETERLINCK

4 Juliet, in *Romeo and Juliet*, by SHAKESPEARE

5 Vera Sappleton, in *The Open Window*, by SAKI

6 *Dracula*, by BRAM STOKER

7 *Peter Pan*, by JAMES M. BARRIE

8 *Enoch Arden*, by TENNYSON

9 Denis Moore, in *Anthony Adverse*, by HERVEY ALLEN

10 Dolohov, in *War and Peace*, by LEO TOLSTOY

71 · Antecedents of ' They '

1 *Sohrab and Rustum*, by MATTHEW ARNOLD

2 The rats, in *The Pied Piper*, by ROBERT BROWNING

3 The seeds, in *Ode to the West Wind*, by SHELLEY

4 *The Walrus and the Carpenter*, by LEWIS CARROLL

5 The cows, in *Little Boy Blue*, by GUY WETMORE CARRYL

6 The dead crewmen, in *The Ancient Mariner*, by COLERIDGE

7 The refugees, from *The Deserted Village*, by GOLDSMITH

8 The rude forefathers, in *Elegy Written in a Country Churchyard*, by GRAY

9 The pilgrims, in *The Landing of the Pilgrim Fathers*, by FELICIA HEMANS

10 Porphyro and Madeline, in *The Eve of St Agnes*, by KEATS

11 *The Owl and the Pussycat*, by LEAR

12 *The Three Kings*, by LONGFELLOW

13 The redcoats, in *The Highwayman*, by ALFRED NOYES

14 The rats, in *God's Judgment on a Wicked Bishop*, by SOUTHEY

15 Philip and Annie, in *Enoch Arden*, by TENNYSON

16 Daffodils, in *I Wandered Lonely as a Cloud*, by WORDSWORTH

72 · Short-story Openings

1 *The Open Window*, by SAKI

2 *The Green Grave and the Black Grave* by MARY LAVIN

3 *The Tell-Tale Heart*, by POE

4 *A Piece of String*, by GUY DE MAUPASSANT

5 *A Scandal in Bohemia*, by CONAN DOYLE

6 *The Gift of the Magi*, by O. HENRY

7 *The Bet*, by ANTON CHEKHOV

8 *A Christmas Carol*, by DICKENS

9 *The Last Class*, by ALPHONSE DAUDET

10 *Gertrude the Governess*, by STEPHEN LEACOCK

73 · Some Famous Sisters

1 Christina Allaby and four unnamed sisters, in *The Way of All Flesh*, by SAMUEL BUTLER

2 Marguerite and Marianne le Patourel, in *Green Dolphin Street*, by ELIZABETH GOUDGE

3 Abby and Martha Brewster, in *Arsenic and Old Lace*, by JOSEPH KESSELRING

4 Jenny and Emmy Blanchard, in *Nocturne*, by FRANK SWINNERTON

5 Constance and Sophia Baines, in *The Old Wives' Tale*, by ARNOLD BENNETT

6 Sophy Crewler Traddles and Caroline, Sarah, Louise, Margaret, Lucy, and four others unnamed, in *David Copperfield*, by DICKENS

7 Elizabeth, Kitty, Mary, Lydia, and Jane Bennet, in *Pride and Prejudice*, by JANE AUSTEN

8 Jo, Beth, Meg, and Amy March, in *Little Women*, by LOUISA M. ALCOTT

9 Cordelia, and Goneril, and Regan, in *King Lear*, by SHAKESPEARE

10 Mabel Stanley, and Edith, Kate, Isabel, and many others unnamed, in *The Pirates of Penzance*, by W. S. GILBERT

74 · Sub-Titles of Well-known Books

1 *Uncle Tom's Cabin*

2 *Vanity Fair*

3 *The Pirates of Penzance*

4 *Lorna Doone*

5 *Silas Marner*

6 *Pamela*

7 *Ben Hur*

8 *Green Mansions*

9 *Twelfth Night*

10 *Jurgen*

11 *From Bed to Worse*

12 *Cass Timberlane*

13 *She Stoops to Conquer*

14 *Cakes and Ale*

15 *Marmion*

16 *Evangeline*

17 *The House of the Dead*

18 *They Stooped to Folly*

19 *In His Steps*

20 *Frankenstein*

75 · Characters Concerned with Flowers

1 Reginald Bunthorne, in *Patience*, by W. S. GILBERT

2 Eliza Doolittle, in *Pygmalion*, by GEORGE BERNARD SHAW

3 *Maud*, by TENNYSON

4 Ophelia, in *Hamlet*, by SHAKESPEARE

5 Rudolph Rassendyll, in *The Prisoner of Zenda*, by ANTHONY HOPE

6 Marguerite Gautier, in *Camille*, by ALEXANDRE DUMAS

7 Nero Wolfe, in many stories by REX STOUT

8 Dr Heidegger, in *Doctor Heidegger's Experiment*, by NATHANIEL HAWTHORNE

9 Alice, in *Through the Looking Glass*, by LEWIS CARROLL

10 Mr Mannering, in *Green Thoughts*, by JOHN COLLIER

76 · 'It's the Syme the Whole World Over'

1 James Steerforth, in *David Copperfield*, by DICKENS

2 Captain Levison, in *East Lynne*, by ELLEN PRICE WOOD

3 Gerald Scales, in *The Old Wives' Tale*, by ARNOLD BENNETT

4 Luke Channel, in *Forever Amber*, by KATHLEEN WINSOR

5 Mr Thornhill, in *The Vicar of Wakefield*, by GOLDSMITH

6 James Windibank, in *A Case of Identity*, by CONAN DOYLE

7 Benjamin Franklin Pinkerton, in *Madame Butterfly*

8 Arthur Donnithorne, in *Adam Bede*, by GEORGE ELIOT

9 Clyde Griffiths, in *An American Tragedy*, by THEODORE DREISER

10 George Osborne, in *Vanity Fair*, by WILLIAM THACKERAY

77 · Last Lines of Sonnets

1 SHAKESPEARE
2 WORDSWORTH
3 DONNE
4 BLUNT
5 WILDE
6 D. G. ROSSETTI
7 BROOKE
8 GRAY
9 MASEFIELD
10 MATTHEW ARNOLD
11 SIDNEY
12 SPENCER
13 BYRON
14 DRAYTON
15 KEATS
16 C. ROSSETTI
17 MILTON
18 SHELLEY
19 E. BROWNING
20 LONGFELLOW

78 · Twice-married Women

1 Florence Udney Parish Adverse, in *Anthony Adverse*, by HERVEY ALLEN

2 Hilda Lessways Cannon Clayhanger, in *These Twain*, by ARNOLD BENNETT

3 Alayne Archer Whiteoak Whiteoak, in *The Whiteoaks of Jalna*, by MAZO DE LA ROCHE

4 Clara Copperfield Murdstone, in *David Copperfield*, by DICKENS

5 Bathsheba Everdene Troy Oak, in *Far from the Madding Crowd*, by THOMAS HARDY

6 Irene Heron Forsyte Forsyte in *The Forsyte Saga*, by JOHN GALSWORTHY

7 Olivia Telworthy Marden, in *Mr Pim Passes By*, by A. A. MILNE

8 Annie Lee Philip Ray, in *Enoch Arden*, by TENNYSON

9 Amelia Sedley Osborne Dobbin, in *Vanity Fair*, by WILLIAM THACKERAY

10 Gertrude, Queen of Denmark, in *Hamlet*, by SHAKESPEARE

79 · Characters who were Disguised

1 Portia, in *The Merchant of Venice*, by SHAKESPEARE
2 Nanki-Poo, in *The Mikado*, by W. S. GILBERT
3 *Huckleberry Finn*, by MARK TWAIN
4 Sherlock Holmes, in *The Adventure of the Empty House*, by CONAN DOYLE
5 *Mlle de Maupin* by THEOPHILE GAUTIER

6 The Actor, in *The Guardsman*, by FRANZ MOLNAR
7 Lord Fancourt Babberly, in *Charley's Aunt*, by BRANDON THOMAS
8 Rosalind, in *As You Like It*, by SHAKESPEARE
9 Saladin, in *The Talisman*, by SCOTT

80 · In the Middle of the Night

1 *Jane Eyre*, by CHARLOTTE BRONTË
2 *Christabel*, by COLERIDGE
3 Rachel Verinder, in *The Moonstone*, by WILKIE COLLINS
4 *David Copperfield*, by DICKENS
5 Frederic, in *The Pirates of Penzance*, by W. S. GILBERT
6 Porphyro, in *The Eve of St Agnes*, by KEATS

7 Natasha, in *War and Peace*, by LEO TOLSTOY
8 Lady Macbeth, in *Macbeth*, by SHAKESPEARE
9 *Dracula*, by BRAM STOKER
10 *Tom Sawyer*, by MARK TWAIN

81 · Fathers and Sons

1 Rustum, in *Sohrab and Rustum*, by MATTHEW ARNOLD
2 Stephen Sorrel, in *Sorrel and Son*, by WARWICK DEEPING
3 Mr Dombey, in *Dombey and Son*, by DICKENS
4 Richard Feverel, in *The Ordeal of Richard Feverel*, by GEORGE MEREDITH

5 *William Tell*, by JOHANN VON SCHILLER
6 *Hamlet*, by SHAKESPEARE
7 *Oedipus Rex*, by SOPHOCLES
8 Mr Shandy, in *Tristram Shandy*, by LAURENCE STERNE
9 George Osborne, in *Vanity Fair*, by WILLIAM THACKERAY
10 *Huckleberry Finn*, by MARK TWAIN

82 · How to Begin a Novel

1 *The Vicar of Wakefield*, by GOLDSMITH
2 *Pilgrim's Progress*, by JOHN BUNYAN
3 *Tristram Shandy*, by LAURENCE STERNE
4 *A Tale of Two Cities*, by DICKENS
5 *Pride and Prejudice*, by JANE AUSTEN

6 *Moby Dick*, by HERMAN MELVILLE
7 *Scaramouche*, by RAFAEL SABATINI
8 *Goodbye, Mr Chips*, by JAMES HILTON
9 *Anthony Adverse*, by HERVEY ALLEN
10 *Babbitt*, by SINCLAIR LEWIS

83 · Requests of Poets

1	THOMAS H. BAYLY	11	JOHN MASEFIELD
2	RUPERT BROOKE	12	TENNYSON
3	ROBERT BROWNING	13	CHRISTIAN ROSSETTI
4	BURNS	14	MILTON
5	BYRON	15	SHAKESPEARE
6	JOHN DONNE	16	SHELLEY
7	SAM WALTER FOSS	17	ROBERT LOUIS STEVENSON
8	THOMAS HOOD	18	CHRISTIAN ROSSETTI
9	BEN JONSON	19	EDMUND WALLER
10	MARLOWE	20	WALT WHITMAN

84 · Gifts in Literature

1 Jean Valjean, in *Les Misérables*, by VICTOR HUGO
2 Portia, in *The Merchant of Venice*, by SHAKESPEARE
3 Della and Jim Young, in *The Gift of the Magi*, by O. HENRY
4 Sheridan Whiteside, in *The Man Who Came to Dinner*, by KAUFMAN and HART
5 Artaban, in *The Story of the Other Wise Man*, by HENRY VAN DYKE
6 Sweets Ramirez, in *Tortilla Flat*, by JOHN STEINBECK
7 Tom Sawyer, by MARK TWAIN
8 Tommy Luck, in *Luck of Roaring Camp*, by BRET HARTE
9 Francie Nolan, in *A Tree Grows in Brooklyn*, by BETTY SMITH
10 Becky Sharp, in *Vanity Fair*, by WILLIAM THACKERAY

85 · Characters who were very Sick

1 Brother François, in *Anthony Adverse*, by HERVEY ALLEN
2 Mark Tapley, in *Martin Chuzzlewit*, by DICKENS
3 Marguerite Gautier, in *Camille*, by ALEXANDRE DUMAS
4 Harry, in *The Snows of Kilimanjaro*, by ERNEST HEMINGWAY
5 Don Birnam, in *The Lost Weekend*, by CHARLES JACKSON
6 Gabriel, in *Evangeline*, by LONGFELLOW.
7 Charles Strickland, in *Moon and Sixpence*, by SOMERSET MAUGHAM
8 Madeline, in *The Fall of the House of Usher*, by EDGAR ALLAN POE
9 Amber St Clare, in *Forever Amber*, by KATHLEEN WINSOR
10 *Nana*, by EMILE ZOLA

86 · Repeated Words and Phrases

1 *The Hill*, by EDGAR LEE MASTERS
2 *The Ancient Mariner*, by COLERIDGE
3 *Bells*, by EDGAR ALLEN POE
4 *The Congo*, by VACHEL LINDSAY
5 *Boots*, by KIPLING
6 *Break, Break, Break*, by TENNYSON
7 *The Wreck of the Hesperus*, by LONGFELLOW

116

8 *Under the Greenwood Tree*, by SHAKESPEARE
9 *The Splendour Falls,* by TENNYSON
10 *Corinna's Going A-Maying*, by HERRICK
11 *The Charge of the Light Brigade*, by TENNYSON
12 *Alexander's Feast*, by DRYDEN
13 *O Captain! My Captain!* by WHITMAN

14 *The Rubáiyát*, by FITZGERALD
15 *The Barrel Organ*, by NOYES
16 *Dixie*, by DAN EMMET
17 *King Lear*, by SHAKESPEARE
18 *Ode on a Grecian Urn*, by KEATS
19 *A Letter from a Girl to Her Own Old Age*, by ALICE MEYNELL
20 *The Song of the Shirt*, by HOOD

87 · Who is ' He '

1 Ben Battle, in *Faithless Nelly Gray*, by THOMAS HOOD
2 The Wedding Guest, in *The Ancient Mariner*, by COLERIDGE
3 The Schoolmaster, in *The Deserted Village*, by OLIVER GOLDSMITH
4 Peterkin, in *The Battle of Blenheim*, by SOUTHEY
5 Sir Ralph the Rover, in *The Inchcape Rock*, by SOUTHEY
6 *Adonais*, by SHELLEY
7 Charlie, in *Charlie, He's My Darling*, by BURNS
8 The Heathen Chinee, Ah Sin, in *Plain Language from Truthful James*, by BRET HARTE

9 *Lochinvar*, by SIR WALTER SCOTT
10 *Richard Cory*, by E. A. ROBINSON
11 *The Village Blacksmith*, by LONGFELLOW.
12 *The Duke of Plaza-Toro*, by W. S. GILBERT
13 Porphyro, in *The Eve of St Agnes*, by KEATS
14 Lord Ullin, in *Lord Ullin's Daughter*, by THOMAS CAMPBELL
15 *Lycidas*, by MILTON
16 The Walrus, in *The Walrus and the Carpenter*, by LEWIS CARROLL

88 · Scrambled Names of Dickens Characters

1 Clara Peggotty
2 Thomas Traddles
3 Uriah Heep
4 Betsey Trotwood
5 Richard Swiveller
6 Wackford Squeers
7 Lucie Manette
8 Tracy Tupman
9 Sydney Carton
10 Edward Murdstone
11 Alfred Jingle
12 Harold Skimpole
13 Augustus Snodgrass
14 Noah Claypole

15 John Jasper
16 Arthur Clennam
17 Martin Chuzzlewit
18 Mark Tapley
19 Wilkins Micawber
20 Cornelia Blimber
21 Silas Wegg
22 Abel Magwitch
23 William Dorrit
24 Paul Dombey
25 Dolly Varden
26 Sampson Brass
27 Thomas Gradgrind
28 Simon Tappertit

29 Samuel Pickwick
30 Nicodemus Boffin
31 Daniel Quilp
32 Susan Nipper
33 Charles Darnay
34 Jerry Cruncher
35 Betsey Prig
36 Esther Summerson
37 James Steerforth
38 Thérèse Defarge

39 Charles Cheeryble
40 Nicholas Nickleby
41 Ninetta Crummles
42 Nathaniel Winkle
43 Ruth Pinch
44 Charity Pecksniff
45 Oliver Twist
46 Edwin Drood
47 Barnaby Rudge
48 Ebenezer Scrooge